Whole life costing

for

water distribution

network management

by

Peter Skipworth, Mark Engelhardt, Adrian Cashman,
Dragan Savic, Adrian Saul, Godfrey Walters

 Thomas Telford

Published by Thomas Telford Publishing, Thomas Telford Ltd, 1 Heron Quay, London E14 4JD.
www.thomastelford.com

Distributors for Thomas Telford books are
USA: ASCE Press, 1801 Alexander Bell Drive, Reston, VA 20191-4400, USA
Japan: Maruzen Co. Ltd, Book Department, 3–10 Nihonbashi 2-chome, Chuo-ku, Tokyo 103
Australia: DA Books and Journals, 648 Whitehorse Road, Mitcham 3132, Victoria

First published 2002

Also available from Thomas Telford Books

Basic water treatment. 3rd edition. Chris Binnie, Martin Kimber and George Smethurst. ISBN 0 7277 3032 0.

A catalogue record for this book is available from the British Library

ISBN: 0 7277 3166 1

Printed and bound in Great Britain by MPG Books, Bodmin, Cornwall

Contents

Foreword

To promote the efficient use of resources in the developed world there is a recognised need to make best use of existing infrastructure. Within this need and in respect of water distribution networks, there are requirements to;

- find the appropriate level of ongoing capital investment in the infrastructure,
- balance operational and capital expenditure,
- consider the impacts on the quality of service received by the customer,
- consider the wider impacts on all stakeholders,
- consider the operation of the distribution network within (pseudo) market constraints in an effort to balance commercial as well as service viability,
- consider the operation of the distribution network within the water delivery and wastewater collection system of which it is a part.

The Whole Life Costing Methodology is aimed at answering these needs through detailed consideration of holistic performance and the explicit linking of costs to the quantities that drive costs, i.e. cost drivers. Two major themes of "Whole Life Cost Accounting" and "Network Performance" have been developed. Within the Methodology, the performance and costs pertaining to the distribution network are considered at elemental and zonal level to find the most economic management scenario.

The WLC accounting framework incorporated within the methodology draws on activity based costing and life cycle analysis to draw out all cost elements and link these to cost drivers. All costs are considered including external costs which are a result of the operator's activities but for which they are not accountable, for example traffic disruption. Monetary penalty costs are imposed in relation to certain aspects of performance represented by performance indicators, many of which are based on the quality of service provided to the customer. These penalty costs are used to constrain performance especially when the scenario management process is automated.

Many of the cost drivers identified by the WLC accounting framework are distribution network performance based. Examples of such quantities would be the number of bursts, the volume of leakage or the length of unlined ferrous main in a particular network. The incorporated network performance framework quantifies these drivers in fulfilling the underlying requirement to link costs to performance. There are six performance sub-modules within the framework; Leakage, Demand Patterns and Projections, Structural Performance, Customer Interruptions, Water Quality, Hydraulic Capacity. Each sub-module quantifies current and future performance and the effect on performance of interventions. An intervention is any action carried out on the network, for example pipe rehabilitation or replacement, or a change in leakage control strategy. The performance sub-modules are designed to take in data and knowledge in order to provide a robust performance assessment. It is often necessary to interpret performance in terms of the quality of service experienced by the customer and this is considered where necessary.

A software based Decision Tool (referred to herein as ExSoft) links the separate yet synchronous cost and performance frameworks. This tool allows the user to investigate "what if" operation and maintenance scenarios, providing decision support via long term costing profiles. Constraints may be imposed on the capital spend at identified time (or intervention) horizons within the period of analysis. A recommended period of analysis is 50 years with intervention horizons set at five yearly intervals. Optimisation can be used as the final step in automating this scenario management process to find least cost solutions with all strategies implicitly considered through explicit definition of intervention options. Such automated processes can trawl through many spatial and temporal decision combinations and find the least WLC management solution within the user-defined performance/risk/cost scenario satisfying the aim of making the best use of the existing pipework infrastructure.

The privatised water industry in England and Wales is regulated under a regime based around comparative competition focussed on serviceability (quality of service at the customer interface). Particular emphasis is placed herein on derivation of the Methodology within this regulatory framework. However, this bias can easily be removed for use of the Methodology in countries where the industry is nationalised or operated under different political constraints.

Authors

Dr Peter J. Skipworth
Pete Skipworth is co-founder and Managing Director of SEAMS, a company specialising in planning the capital maintenance and operation of distributed assets based on the principles of whole life costing. Previously an academic at the University of Sheffield (UK) working closely with the water industry, Pete's focus has been on the operation of underground sewerage and water distribution assets. He has won prizes for artificial intelligence modelling, novel flowrate measurement and sewer ancillary design.

Dr Mark O. Engelhardt
Dr Mark Engelhardt is co-founder of SEAMS, a company specialising in applying the Whole Life Costing Approach to determine the long-term expenditure requirements of distributed networks. Prior to SEAMS' inception, Dr Engelhardt spent seven years undertaking academic research in Australia and England. His prime research interest remains the development of decision support for application in the water industry. Dr Engelhardt's role within the research team required him to author the example software presented within the book. Before his research based at the University of Exeter, Dr Engelhardt undertook his undergraduate and doctoral degree at the University of Adelaide, Australia.

Mr Adrian Cashman
Adrian Cashman studied civil engineering at Kings College London. On graduating he joined a major UK contractor, getting his first taste of water engineering working on a stormwater sewer project. In 1982, he joined the Department of Water Affairs in Namibia, developing water resources and urban and rural water supply. For the next 12 years he held various positions including Head of Design and Chief of Water Supply Operations. After five years as a consultant in the water industry, he changed direction and took a masters' degree in environmental economics. He has been responsible for developing the whole life cost accounting framework and its application to distribution systems and is currently studying for a PhD at the University of Sheffield, researching regulation, sustainability and accountability in the water industry.

Professor Dragan A. Savic
Dragan Savic is Professor of Hydroinformatics at Exeter University and a Chartered (Professional) Engineer with over eighteen years of research, teaching and consulting experience in various water-engineering disciplines. His interests include developing and applying computer modelling and optimisation techniques to water engineering systems, with particular application to the operation and design of water supply and distribution networks. He jointly heads Exeter University's Centre for Water Systems. Professor Savic is currently serving as Associated Editor of the Journal of Water Resources Planning and Management (ASCE). He is also serving on the Editorial Boards of Water and Maritime Engineering (ICE), Water International and the Journal of Hydroinformatics (IWA). He has published over 150 research/professional papers and reports.

Professor Adrian J. Saul

Prof. Saul has over twenty-five years post-doctoral experience working in the area of urban storm drainage. He is currently Professor of Water Engineering at the University of Sheffield, a position he has held for the past 12 years. His internationally leading research expertise spans a wide range of topics, ranging from the quality of drinking water to the performance of sewer ancillary structures and their impact on receiving waters. Over 150 publications have been made from this work and Professor Saul also has an excellent track record in the transfer of the research outputs into industry practices.

Professor Godfrey A. Walters

After graduating from Cambridge University in 1969, Professor Walters spent seven years in the construction industry, with Tarmac Construction, with Manchester Corporation Waterworks and finally with water engineering consultants, Binnie and Partners. He then studied for a PhD at Liverpool University, exploring numerical optimisation in water system design. He was appointed to a lectureship at the University of Exeter in 1979, where he is presently Professor of Water Engineering in the School of Engineering and Computer Science. Professor Walters jointly heads the internationally renowned Centre for Water Systems. He is a member of the Institution of Civil Engineers, and of the Chartered Institution of Water and Environmental Management, and retains close links with the water industry.

Acknowledgements

The authors gratefully acknowledge the financial support by the UK Engineering and Physical Sciences Research Council of the work reported herein. This project was carried out in collaboration with and under the direction of a committee of water industry professionals from Yorkshire Water Services, North West Water, Thames Water Utilities, ONDEO Services (Lyonnaise des eaux), Geodesys and Ewan Group plc. The individuals and companies are thanked for their contributions and enthusiastic and consistent support of the work.

CHAPTER ONE
Introduction

In respect of a service facility, Whole Life Costing (WLC) considers all the costs (private and social) that accrue to its initiation, provision, operation, maintenance, servicing and decommissioning, over its useful life. Through the development of a costing framework based on activity based costing (ABC) and life cycle assessment (LCA), and through detailed consideration of network performance, the WLC Approach to Distribution Network Management links costs to performance through the quantities that drive costs – the cost drivers. Thus, as performance or output changes as a result of an action or operation, so the changes in costs are tracked.

The WLC Approach to Distribution Network Management (known from hereon as the "Methodology") aims to achieve the lowest network provision and operating cost, when all costs are considered, to achieve standards enforced by regulation or otherwise. Cognisance is taken of all relevant costs – direct and indirect, private and societal – in order to balance the needs of the service supplier, the customer, society and the environment in a sustainable manner.

Water distribution networks are operated under economic conditions and political systems which have a bearing on capital investment and operational decisions. This must be taken account of in the Methodology. The privatised, regulated water industry operated in England and Wales is used as a backdrop to facilitate the development of the Methodology. However, the resulting bias can easily be removed for use of the Methodology where the industry is nationalised or operated under different political constraints. Wherever the network, the constraints on operation and investment will invariably be based around the cost and the quality of service denoted by similar performance indicators.

Within the water industry in England and Wales, expenditure is regulated in order to meet customer standards and to protect the environment. This is against a background of optimising the utilisation and performance of existing assets to minimise the cost to customers and maximise shareholder returns to ensure the industry remains financially viable. Within the five-year asset management planning (AMP) cycles, spending is planned to meet regulatory requirements based on the use of the best available techniques and technology to meet the challenges faced by the industry. Integrating performance objectives, whilst balancing the trade-offs between costs, benefits and risks, has to be achieved within the operator's statutory and legal boundaries. The WLC approaches offer the ideal platform to complete such analyses.

The decisions in the operation and maintenance of the assets of a water distribution network require the operator to balance costs with future performance including the quality of service experienced by the customer. The Methodology is born from a concern that approaches to expenditure on the maintenance of assets previously adopted by operators may not have been entirely adequate and grounded in sound economic principles. Proper justification for pipe renewal is unlikely to be driven by a single operational consideration (e.g. leakage), but by an array of considerations including structural failure, water quality performance, leakage and hydraulic performance, much of which affects the quality of service. The Methodology offers an appropriate platform for inclusive appraisals. Scenarios are developed for future operation and maintenance to evaluate the relative impact these have on the future cost stream and network performance. The Methodology offers the advantages that;

- monetary costs are used to give a universal understanding,
- the impact of decision making on relative cost effectiveness becomes transparent and therefore fully auditable to external reporters,
- it provides an economically based rationale to asset management,
- it considers both costs and performance over extended periods,
- it provides the flexibility to extend the analysis to incorporate sustainability issues related to resource use and impacts on the environment and society.

The challenges in implementation of the Methodology include;

- accounting for the role of regulation,
- requiring risk to be assessed in relation to the Methodology,
- determining the (geographical, temporal and cost) boundaries,
- explicitly assigning the costs at the appropriate decision level, e.g. district meter area (DMA),[1] of individual assets,
- determining what are the societal cost components and linking them to an analysis of cost drivers,
- adequately predicting the performance of the network over an extended time period.

The remainder of this introductory chapter is given over to explaining the major components of the Methodology, these being the WLC Accounting Module, the Performance Module, and the Decision Tool which links the first two modules together as the "Scenario Manager". Before this, Section 1.1 provides background on the regulatory regime in England and Wales. The final Section of Chapter 1 deals with Risk.

1.1   Regulation of the Water Industry in England and Wales

1.1.1   The Regulatory Framework

The current regulation of the Water Industry in England and Wales is by three principal regulators;

- The Office of Water Services (Ofwat)   economic regulator
- The Environment Agency (EA)   environmental regulator
- The Drinking Water Inspectorate (DWI)   potable water quality regulator

---

[1] An area of a distribution network typically containing 2000 to 5000 properties (NWC/DoE, 1980) which is specifically defined, e.g. by the closure of valves, and in which the quantities of water entering and leaving the area are metered.

All three are established as statutory bodies to give practical implementation of the legal requirements of Parliament and policy aims of the government of the day. The sponsor Ministry of Ofwat and the EA is the Department for Environment, Food and Rural Affairs (DEFRA), which took over from the Department of the Environment, Transport and the Regions (DETR) in June 2001. The DWI is part of DEFRA.

1.1.1.1   Economic Regulation

Ofwat was created under the 1989 Water Act (Privatisation) as a non-ministerial government department directly responsible to Parliament, with independent powers under the 1991 Water Industry Act. The primary duties of the Director General (DG) of Ofwat are to ensure that;

- the functions of water and sewerage companies, as specified in the 1989 Water Act, are properly carried out,
- companies are able to finance their proper functions, in particular by securing a reasonable rate of return on their capital.

The DG has a number of secondary duties including obligations to;

- ensure that customers' interests are protected,
- provide incentives to reduce costs and pass savings on to customers,
- facilitate competition.

These duties ensure the primacy of Ofwat over other regulators. In carrying out its functions, Ofwat consults and takes advice but is not bound in its decision making. The fact that it is responsible directly to Parliament puts it in a powerful, independent position.

1.1.1.2   Environmental Regulation

The Environment Act of 1995 set out the principle aim of the Environment Agency (EA), which is to protect, or enhance the environment (taken as a whole) so as to contribute to sustainable development. The EA is a non-departmental public body (NDPB) with a Board appointed by and responsible to Ministers. The EA advises the Government on environmental programmes and improvements required to meet the needs of EU Directives and national legislation. Its specific responsibilities include pollution control, management of water resources and responsibility for all "controlled waters" under the terms of the Water Resources Act (1991). It exercises these functions through a system of licences and permits as well as the setting of water quality objectives.

1.1.1.3   Potable Water Quality Regulation

The Drinking Water Inspectorate (DWI) is part of DEFRA and as such is responsible to the Secretary of State. Its role is to ensure that water companies comply with their statutory duty to supply water fit for human consumption by monitoring the results of mandatory sampling. Legal standards are set out in the Water Quality Regulations, most of which are derived from the EU Drinking Water Directive. In turn, the Directive was derived in accordance with the WHO Guidelines (Scientific Committee on Toxicology and Ecotoxicology). In addition to the mandatory sampling activities, which are reactive by nature, DWI has launched a number of proactive initiatives, such as water quality management plans (DWI, 1998) and drinking water aspects of serviceability (Ofwat, 2001) relating to water supply networks.

1.1.2   The Role of Regulation

"Regulation" has become an all-encompassing term to cover a wide array of political and economic mechanisms. In reality, regulation seeks to arrange, direct and govern in such a way as to produce actions that conform to a norm. It is a convenient way to administer public policy as it usually does not involve direct taxation or government spending to achieve its goals. Regulation can be divided into "economic" and "social" regulation. Economic regulation seeks to address issues related to the functioning of a market whilst social regulation deals with the interests of individuals, health and safety and environment related goals.

The water companies in England and Wales, as they are presently constituted, are natural monopolies within their geographic areas. It is largely to prevent the potential abuse of monopoly power that the economic regulator has been put in place. In the absence of market forces that provide incentives for the self-regulation of behaviour, companies might seek to maximise profits at the expense of the quality of service and value for money to the customer. One of the functions of Ofwat, therefore, is to provide and implement instruments that can act as surrogates for market competition and conditions. To facilitate this function, use is made of comparative competition to improve company performance in order to promote the provision of better services at lower costs. Within or apart from comparative competition, Ofwat regulates company performance using instruments based around;

- regulatory accounts and annual returns on financial performance and expenditure,
- the quality of service experienced by the customer,[2]
- leakage and water efficiency,
- the supply/demand balance,
- the maintenance of serviceability,
- water and sewerage service unit costs and relative efficiency.

Social regulation is required for similar reasons to economic regulation. In the absence of customer choice there need to be safeguards that ensure the quality and safety of the product. Water has to be safe and fit to drink. Additionally, the processes and activities involved in its production and (wastewater) disposal must conform to acceptable standards. For regulation to be successful there have to be accompanying penalties for non-compliance, set in such a way as to provide dynamic incentives that, at a minimum, encourage compliance and for some aspects encourage exceedance.

In summary, therefore, Regulation should be seen as a process that includes;

- the formation of goals/objectives,
- systems to monitor compliance,
- the provision of incentives for the achievement of goals.

---

[2] Measured in England and Wales by nine levels of service indicators – DG1 to DG9 – for example, reflecting the number of interruptions to service, the frequency of sewer flooding incidents, and the quality of response to customer contacts.

1.1.3   Regulation within the Methodology

The first part of the regulatory process, the formation or setting of goals, has an important role to play within the Methodology. Goals relate to network performance requirements and cover levels of service, leakage, supply/demand balance and serviceability indicators. They are taken as being aspects of performance that in a competitive environment an efficient operator would seek to maximise at minimum cost to the customer. The role of the regulator is to set goals at a level that the customer desires. The regulator then goes on to consider what the further implications of the goals are and gives guidance as to what factors need to be taken into consideration. The view is that network assets must be maintained in such a condition that they can provide an economic and efficient service. Ofwat is active in developing a framework for assessing capital maintenance requirements as well as policy on the economic appraisal of long term capital needs. Thus, in issuing guidelines (e.g. Ofwat, 2000a) the regulator has interpreted the scope of his or her obligations and duties in a broad and comprehensive manner. The practical effect of this is that it draws into the regulatory process the steps required to demonstrate how goals/objectives will be achieved. This has implications because of the need to demonstrate a linkage between serviceability and expenditure, something that the Methodology is geared to deliver.

The serviceability requirements, or the need to ensure that they do not deteriorate over time, are picked up within the Methodology through the use of financial penalty costs. When a serviceability measure (or the proxies identified in Chapters 6, 7 and 8) deteriorates and exceeds threshold levels, penalty costs are applied. Details on penalty costs are in Chapter 4. Thus the solutions derived using the Methodology are economically constrained by the inclusion of regulatory goal related penalties. These are proxies for market forces as intended by the regulators through the implementation of such initiatives as comparative competition.

Customers themselves generate other costs faced by the water company. These costs are associated with the interaction between the customers and the companies that supply them. Ofwat has placed emphasis on these contacts with a requirement on the companies to ensure that all contacts are dealt with promptly and appropriately. Regulation requires, through defined DG measures, that the water companies report annually the number of contacts and the time taken to respond to these queries. Four of the nine DG measures are associated with the number and responses of contacts, complaints and queries. Distinction is made between those via mail and those via telephone.

1.2   The Methodology

1.2.1   The Principle

A methodology has been developed to enable the WLC of a distribution network to be calculated. The basic principle behind the Methodology is the identification of all entries in the WLC accounts, and further the identification of the quantity that drives each entry, the cost driver, such that a full accrual can be attached to each entry. The relationship between the total cost corresponding to an entry as a function of its cost driver is given in Figure 1.1.

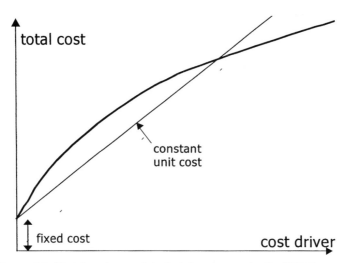

Figure 1.1: Total cost associated with an entry in the WLC accounts

For example, an entry may be the "cost of leaked water", the corresponding cost driver being the "volume of leaked water". The unit cost of the leaked water corresponds to the gradient of the relationship between the total cost of leaked water and the cost driver (the volume). Clearly, the unit cost will vary with the volume of leaked water. Further, a change in operational strategy, or a change in efficiency, may lead to a shift or change in this relationship.

A further example of a WLC accounts entry is the "cost of mains replacement" which is a function of its cost driver, the "length of mains replaced". Obviously, the unit cost will differ based on the diameter, material and situation of the pipe. In addition, as the length replaced (cost driver) increases, progressing along the x-axis in Figure 1.1, economies of scale would be gained and the gradient of the relationship would therefore decrease. A fixed cost associated with mains replacement would be reflected in Figure 1.1 by a migration of the curve in the positive y-direction.

In respect of any interventions on the network, for example pipe replacement or an operational intervention such as a change in leakage control strategy, the basic WLC principle described above can be generalised as shown in Figure 1.2. Firstly, a period of analysis for application of the Methodology is identified with time horizons spaced throughout the period when interventions can be made. Starting in the top left-hand corner in Figure 1.2, considering an "Intervention" made on the network at a given time horizon, the cost of the intervention accrues to the "WLC Accounts" at the particular time horizon. In addition, the intervention (e.g. a pipe replacement) will affect performance (e.g. burst frequency, leakage, water quality) and hence "Cost Drivers" at the current time horizon and at all the preceding time horizons in the period of analysis. These modified "Cost Drivers" act on "Costs" which in turn accrue to the "WLC Accounts".

A similar process to that outlined in Figure 1.2 can be envisioned for "non-interventions". If the operator decides to "do nothing", although no costs will accrue directly to the "WLC Accounts", changes in the performance of the network with time, for example due to deterioration of the assets, will affect the "Cost Drivers" which act on the variable, penalty and fixed "Costs" throughout the period of analysis.

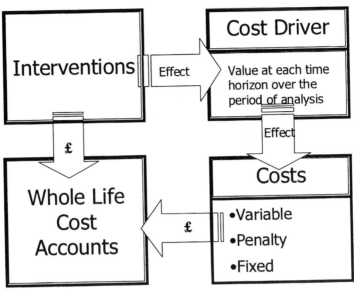

Figure 1.2: Fitting the elements together

1.2.2 The Framework for the Methodology

The Methodology has been configured according to the diagram in Figure 1.3.

The "WLC Accounting" Module represents an accounting process that attempts to identify and report all costs. Entries in the WLC accounts have identified cost drivers.

The "Network Performance" Module represents the process whereby the network in question is characterised in terms of both its attributes and performance. Its attributes are the physical description of each pipe element that makes up the network and their connectivity. This information is brought into the Methodology via a geographical information system (GIS). Many of the cost drivers identified in the WLC accounts are performance based. Therefore, the "Network Performance" Module contains models, including a hydraulic model, that are able to simulate different aspects of performance with time under changing conditions, for example due to deterioration in the assets, changes in demand, and due to interventions. In this way, quantities can be attached to performance based cost drivers.

In summary, all costs and the quantities that drive them are identified in the "Whole Life Cost Accounting" and "Network Performance" Modules respectively. It must then be determined how this information is used in deriving management scenarios for operating and maintaining the network. This function is fulfilled by the "Decision Tool" element in Figure 1.3, which assimilates and links the information and models in the cost and performance modules. Optimisation can be used in the "Decision Tool" to automate the scenario management process in order to find the most appropriate, for example the least WLC, management scenario.

Each of the three elements in Figure 1.3 is discussed in more detail in Sections 1.3.1 to 1.3.7.

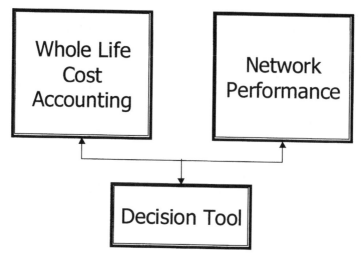

Figure 1.3: The Framework for the Methodology

1.2.3   Boundaries

Geographical (or operational) boundaries must be identified for application of the Methodology. In addition, to make the Methodology tractable, temporal and cost boundaries must be identified.

1.2.3.1   *Geographical*

In order to make the Methodology tractable, the geographical boundary is set downstream of the service reservoir with costs included to describe the interaction of the network with the upstream system. The downstream cut off point for the WLC methodology is in effect the first point of practicable use for the customer – serviceability is measured at the customer interface.

The Methodology and pilot software tool (ExSoft) is recommended for a Water Supply Zone (WSZ) scale of application and the Methodology is set out accordingly herein. A WSZ is the next level of geographical aggregation up from a district meter area (DMA), i.e. it is an aggregation of several DMAs. This is referred to differently in different organisations.

1.2.3.2   *Temporal*

The primary purpose of expenditure on water distribution is to maintain network performance and the quality of service received by customers. An implication of this is that there is an indefinite "useful life" for a network. The "useful life" is constantly being altered by the way in which the operator maintains a network and consequently this will affect performance. So, within the Methodology, a period of analysis has to be determined that is long enough for the effects of expenditures on performance to be manifest through the system but not so long as to trivialise them when discounted (if discounting is being applied to costs). It is for this reason that a period of analysis of 50 years is being proposed. *Period of analysis* therefore takes over from the "useful life", depreciation period or accounting lifespan as a more realistic and pragmatic bound. With respect to discounting in net present value calculations, it is often a matter of subjective judgement and that the most appropriate approach may be to have some mid-range estimate of discount rate accompanied by a sensitivity analysis.

Under some circumstances, for example where expenditure is intentionally distributed over a period of analysis and is considered at 2002 prices, the time value of money will not be considered.

1.2.3.3   *Cost*

Although it is the performance and hence the costs of operation and maintenance of the distribution network that is the main focus, the network cannot be considered in isolation as it is part of an integrated system. How the distribution network is operated and performs affects systems both upstream (abstraction, treatment and transfer) and downstream (wastewater collection, treatment and disposal). Given, for example, that the cost of treated water provision is interdependent with the upstream system, the interconnected nature of costs must be explicitly reflected in the accounting framework. However, to make the approach tractable "at-boundary on-costs" are often used.

The operation of a distribution network can have wide impacts on, for example, the environment. Associated industries, for example pipe manufacturers, produce waste and emissions and use raw materials. Similarly, the producers of these raw materials produce waste and emissions and the chain goes on. To make the WLC approach tractable, the purchase costs of inputs required by the operator are considered to reflect these impacts.

To be realistic and to take account of the variations present in any operator's distribution network, costings are disaggregated. The level of disaggregation for unit cost accounting is at the water supply zone (WSZ) level.

1.3   Book Overview

Chapters 2 to 12 of this book are arranged with reference to the general methodology and the three main themes of "Whole Life Cost Accounting", "Network Performance" and the "Decision Tool" – in accordance with Figure 1.3.

1.3.1   Whole Life Cost Accounting

The WLC Accounting part of the Methodology is covered by Chapters 2 to 5. Chapter 2 is a literature review offering background on Whole Life Costing, Life Cycle Assessment and Activity Based Costing. Chapter 3 discusses Environmental Impact Assessments with respect to distribution networks. Chapters 4 and 5 introduce the WLC Accounting Methodology and its practical application respectively.

1.3.1.1   *Background*

The concept of WLC within an engineering context is nearly 20 years old and first emerged in the field of buildings and structures. It grew out of a recognition that the initial cost of a structure was but one part of the overall costs over the lifetime of a structure, and that undue attention to minimising initial cost could, in fact, lead to greater overall cost. More holistic approaches have been advocated and adopted, and their application to other areas has expanded. WLC is now a widely advocated approach to the provision of public sector services, finding a resonance in such initiatives as Public Private Partnerships (PPPs), and Private Finance Initiatives (PFIs) and Best Value Practice as well as in BS/ISO 15686. Other sectors that have adopted this approach include Roads and Transportation and Higher Education. Interest in WLC in the water sector first started in the mid 1990s, especially in its potential application to the rehabilitation of underground assets. Recent concerns over the need for better justification of investment in underground assets have given an added impetus to WLC as a tool to address these issues.

ABC was developed during the 1980s from a recognition of the limitations of traditional cost accounting in dealing with cost elements such as overheads in a rational manner. Within ABC, cost drivers, which may be numerous, relate activities to production. The cost drivers must provide an adequate explanation of outputs whilst at the same time being measurable and change sensitive. The development of the approach was predominantly in process based industry but has now found much wider application.

LCA emerged from manufacturing based industries. It seeks to measure the environmental burden of products and/or materials used in a process. It evaluates the material inputs and outputs of a process to uncover the cost drivers and causes of the environmental burdens as well as the consequential or hidden costs that arise from them and that are not usually accounted for.

1.3.1.2   Cost Identification

The WLC methodology is inclusive of the private costs which accrue to an operator and is also optionally inclusive of what are variously referred to as public costs, social and environmental costs, societal costs or externalities. The accounting methodology seeks to attribute costs to unique performance drivers (actions or operations) that give rise to them. By treating costs in this way it redistributes what might be called indirect, hidden or overhead costs such that they become direct costs. Adopting a long term approach tends to blur the distinction between operational and capital expenditure. Within the Methodology, *all* expenditures are seen as being required to support and maintain operation of a network. This emphasises the link between investment and performance.

1.3.1.3   Internalisation of Costs

In many parts of the developed world, the water industries are being led towards internalising their external costs. In other words, the industry is becoming responsible for carrying the costs that to date have fallen on society. This is apparent through the prosecutions that have been sought in respect of a number of water quality incidents being reported by the companies to the Drinking Water Inspectorate (DWI, 2000b). The pressure put on companies in the middle to late 1990s to consider the environmental impact of leakage in their estimates of the "economic levels of leakage" is a further example. There is no reason to believe that this trend will not continue, as internalising all costs is a step toward addressing sustainability. The WLC methodology has the flexibility to include externalities such as social and environmental costs within its framework. This gives the user the ability to explore the impact of such inclusions and to demonstrate the implications this might have for the operation and management of distribution systems, and for types and levels of investment strategies. This echoes one of the requirements of the EU Water Framework Directive Article 5, which recognises that *"environmental and resource costs associated with damage or negative impact on the environment should be taken into account".*

Whilst there is a recognition of the existence of social and environmental costs (externalities) and their potential influence on cost effective solutions, there is uncertainty over whether and how to incorporate and quantify these costs. Externalities have to be considered within a situation specific context and there are techniques available to value them (DETR, 2000). Unless specific costing studies are carried out the accuracy of the external cost values may be called into question.

1.3.1.4   Structure and Elements of Cost Allocation

Much of Chapter 4 is given over to the detailed derivation of the structure and elements of the cost accounting module. The development of the module was based upon Ofwat's Regulatory Accounting Guidelines (RAG) 4.01 (Ofwat, 1992) allocation of operational activities. Whilst RAG 4.01 considers activities at the level of a company the approach adopted involves the devolution of these costs and activities to a much lower level and one based upon the operational realities of a company. Thus, it recognises that activities take place within a geographical context related to the nature and extent of the distribution networks. The ultimate choice of level of devolution lies with the operator though for practical purposes the level of WSZ is suggested as a sensible unit for application of the Methodology.

Within the Methodology, a distinction is made between Resources and Treatment, and Distribution with the former providing the input cost of water into a network. This allows the effects of changes in the distribution network on resource use and treatment and the concomitant costs to be accounted for. The costs in the distribution network are designated as being either;

(a) the "normal" cost of water supply (including water quality), or,

(b) the costs associated with leakage, or,

(c) the costs associated with bursts (structural failure).

"Normal" operation is taken to include all those activities that are required to provide a normal service to customers and includes such activities and events that can be foreseen and planned for, i.e. the costs can be predicted with a reasonable degree of certainty and accuracy. This does include implicit (and often unrecognised, normative) assumptions of risk associated with these activities. A lower level of risk associated with a certain activity would be correlated with higher expenditure on it.

The costs associated with bursts include provision for their repair as well as other activities that result from bursts occurring. This is separate from any network rehabilitation that comes about as a result of a management decision. In contrast, the costs associated with leakage do not include any provision for repair, just those associated with detection and other aspects of leakage control. Leakage may be an important motivator for management decisions regarding rehabilitation works programmes.

A feature of the methodology is that it allows the inclusion of assumed penalties associated with certain levels of non-compliant performance, for example leakage targets. This represents an assessment on the part of the operator of the financial consequences associated with non-compliance.

1.3.2   Network Performance

The WLC accounting framework has identified many performance-based cost drivers. These must be characterised and assigned quantities via appropriate performance models and this is the purpose of the "Network Performance" module. The holistic track of the Methodology has resulted in a holistic performance evaluation framework as detailed in Figure 1.4 which shows six performance sub-modules in octagonal boxes.

Within the Methodology there is a need to;

i)   *identify methods of performance evaluation*

> This is the primary aim of Chapters 6, 7 and 8. Methods are presented which allow performance to be understood and quantified based on knowledge and data, in order to assign values to cost drivers.

ii)   *quantify current performance and how this will change with time*

> The performance evaluation methods from *i)* can be applied to understand current performance and project how this will change with time.

iii)   *consider different aspects of performance interactively*

> Significant overlap exists between the performance elements in Figure 1.4. The lines of delimitation are made clear such that different performance aspects and their attached costs accrue only once and in the appropriate place (i.e. there is no double accounting).

iv)   *quantify the effect of interventions*

> The effect of interventions must be quantified. For example a pipe replacement will affect a range of performance attributes, e.g. burst rate, leakage, and the potential for different water quality failures to occur. Interventions at operational level, i.e. a change in leakage control strategy, will affect leakage, overall demand in the network and therefore its hydraulic capacity.

In summary, each performance module must quantify current and future performance and the effect on performance of interventions.

1.3.2.1   Asset Condition, Performance and Serviceability

For the purposes of this book, in respect of distribution network assets the following definitions are used:

Condition: the physical condition or state of an asset

Performance: the behaviour of the asset(s)

Serviceability: a measure of the quality of service received by customers and the ability of the assets (and their operator) to maintain the quality of service[3]

The water industry in England and Wales is centred around satisfying serviceability requirements. To be able to predict changes in serviceability measures with time and intervention activity, within the performance sub-modules it is often necessary to analyse and model performance and translate this to serviceability.

Condition data is never directly considered in the performance evaluation. However, a number of the performance sub-modules are based on the estimation of condition and how this will change with time. For example, the hydraulic roughness of ferrous mains (i.e. the condition of the internal bore) can be considered in the performance

---

[3] When considering serviceability in England and Wales, its definition is inextricably tied to that given by the economic regulator, Ofwat.

evaluation framework in its impact on the ability of the network to satisfy hydraulic requirements.

1.3.2.2   Performance Evaluation Framework

Defining and assessing the performance of a water distribution network as part of the Methodology requires consideration of many different aspects of performance. As such, the final tool (ExSoft) needs to be built around a computer platform that offers the functionality required to store the network attribute data for the evaluation of performance. The GIS and Hydraulic Model elements of Figure 1.4 represent the integration of the Methodology within the hydraulic modelling and GIS environments. These aspects are largely dealt with in Chapter 10. The performance sub-modules in the octagonal boxes in Figure 1.4 are to ensure that the appropriate aspects of a network's performance are evaluated in order to assign quantities to cost drivers. As indicated, the performance sub-modules can be split into three groups; Supply and Demand, Structural Performance, and Water Quality. These groups of performance sub-modules are the respective subjects of Chapters 6, 7 and 8.

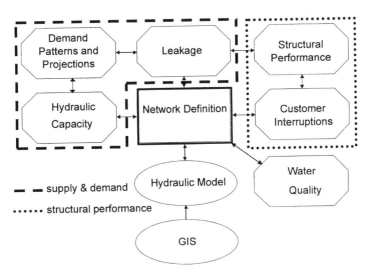

Figure 1.4: Network Definition

Within the Supply and Demand group (Chapter 6), the aim of the *Leakage* performance sub-module is to quantify the effects on leakage of different control and pipe replacement or rehabilitation strategies. The leakage volume accrues to the *Demand Patterns and Projections* sub-module which deals with the changes in demands in the network with time. The *Hydraulic Capacity* sub-module deals with the ability of a network to deliver an adequate hydraulic service considering the changes in demand (from the *Demand Patterns and Projections* sub-module) and changes in the hydraulic conductivity of pipes as they deteriorate with time or are replaced.

The risk of different water quality failures is dependent on pipe description and the risk therefore changes with pipe replacement or rehabilitation. Additionally, proactive management of networks or changes in treatment will to some extent mitigate water quality failure risks. The role of *Water Quality* is considered in a separate performance sub-module detailed in Chapter 8.

It is required within the *Structural Performance* sub-module to understand and assign characteristic failure rates to each pipe (or pipe group) and project these in time. In respect of this requirement, Chapter 8 outlines a detailed methodology whereby failure rates (bursts/year) are assigned based on an analysis of asset and historical failure data commonly available in water companies. The consequence of mains failure in terms of the number of and the length of time for which services are interrupted is dealt with in the *Customer Interruptions* sub-module. Customer interruptions are considered part of the consequence (or as a sub-set) of structural failure. A rational data-driven method for estimating this consequence and a more exhaustive hydraulic modelling based approach are outlined.

In Chapters 6 to 8, in respect of each performance sub-module, brief literature reviews are presented prior to the derivation of the performance evaluation methodologies. Sub-sections are given over to clarifying the relationships between the modules.

1.3.3   Decision Tool

The "Decision Tool" represents the integration of the "WLC Accounting" and "Network Definition" modules onto a single computational platform. It allows consolidation of the information within each module, providing the ability to assimilate a large amount of disparate information. Thus it allows the implications of each module (and their constituent elements) to be assessed holistically, and traced through to their financial conclusion. As such it provides a basis for WLC decision making.

Chapters 9 through 12 detail the utilisation of the Methodology as a decision support tool. Details on the decision support provided by WLC, the development of WLC software, its implications in terms of hardware and the steps involved in automating such a decision making process are provided. Throughout, each step is demonstrated through **ExSoft**, a pilot software tool developed in parallel to the Methodology.

1.3.4   Assimilating WLC Knowledge to provide Decision Support

The Methodology has been developed on the premise of the ultimate linking of the costs identified in the "WLC Accounting" module to the quantities reflecting performance (cost drivers) calculated in the "Network Performance" module. Chapter 9 provides an introduction to the bringing together of the two modules onto a single platform, denoted in Figure 1.3 as the "Decision Tool". Once onto this platform, the established links give a basis by which WLC can provide decision support. As background to this, a historical review of the decision support provided in determining expenditure required in water distribution networks is presented. Essentially, the single platform allows a decision maker to investigate amongst other things, the sensitivity of each cost or performance parameter and any defined performance/cost/risk scenario.

Ultimately, the ramifications in terms of the trade-off between capital and operating expenditure need to be identified. Because of the large number of possibilities in terms of capital, maintenance and operational interventions over the period of analysis, a further level of decision support is required to identify the most appropriate (e.g. least WLC) strategy. This extra support is achieved by automating the scenario investigation through incorporation of an automated search technique.

1.3.5 Developing WLC Software

When considering the integration of the "WLC Accounting" and "Network Performance" modules and subsequent decision support, the software implications of this proposition cannot be escaped. WLC brings together data that requires analysis from disparate databases within a water company. Chapter 10 investigates the requirements placed by each of the sub-modules in this respect.

The basic structure of ExSoft is discussed, investigating the links it makes to external databases to bring in the data required by the accounting scheme and performance modelling encapsulated by the Methodology. As such, ExSoft represents one alternative by which the various difficulties encountered when discussing generic WLC software can be overcome.

1.3.6 Scenario Management: Case Study

The overall Methodology is demonstrated in Chapter 11 by applying ExSoft to a case study system. The system investigated has been taken from a real world system in England. The WLC Accounting module and the various performance sub-modules were populated with representative data. This allows various scenarios to be investigated and the subsequent links established within the "Network Performance" and "WLC Accounting" module to be witnessed.

Chapter 11 also investigates the ways in which a WLC analysis can be reported. By just considering the cost streams over the period of analysis, a number of allocating schemes across activities, for example, normal operation, bursts and leakage (as in RAG 4.01), can be utilised to present the results. Such presentation allows the cost consequences of any operation and maintenance scenario to be tracked across the whole spectrum of costs.

1.3.7 Automation of the Decision Making Process

The relationships, i.e. the links between the costs and the drivers, should allow for every scenario to be considered and assessed both in terms of their WLC and distribution network performance. Automating a decision making process requires the decision maker to explicitly define the objective, each decision and the alternatives available in each decision. The objective relates to that which is to be achieved. In the case of WLC, the simplest objective is to minimise the WLC given the cost constraints placed on performance. Conversely, performance can be maximised for a constrained expenditure (capital or otherwise). Decision variables represent a particular asset (or asset groups) where a decision can be made to meet the defined objective. Decision alternatives (pipe rehabilitation or operational) may be constrained by the operating regime of the company or the options available within the market. For example, a water network may be defined by a set of DMAs. The decision variables may be the leakage activities to be undertaken. Thus, the decision alternatives are represented by the set of activities (i.e. the available leakage detection strategies) that could be undertaken within the DMA.

The chosen search technique incorporated in ExSoft is the genetic algorithm (GA). In the past, this optimisation technique has been utilised for a wide range of water distribution related problems, including the scheduling of rehabilitation works given a variety of performance constraints.

Chapter 12 presents each step that must be undertaken to automate the WLC decision making process, once again utilising ExSoft as a working example. It culminates in the application of the GA to the case study system introduced in Chapter 11.

1.4   Risk

Risk considers the effect of uncertainty and its role in influencing the outcome of any decision making process. It is implied within the Methodology through the explicit and common definition applied to risk, namely that it is the product of probability and consequence. WLC is first and foremost an accounting process. Each cost is identified and associated, where applicable, with its driver. Each activity has its consequence ascribed in values of its cost driver ("Network Performance") and cost ("WLC Accounting"). The probability of an activity taking place may be stochastic in nature. For example, a main's failure and hence the requirement to repair it may be influenced by meteorological conditions.

There is no steadfast answer as to how the risk of each element should be considered within the Methodology. Decisions pertaining to water are invariably based on statutory requirements. The ACS (1998) report commented on how risk is considered within statutory requirements. Statutes generally fall under the following headings:

- *Hazard Based Standards*: Mandate requires hazards to be regulated without regard to cost factors or the current availability of suitable control factors (e.g. water quality).

- *Technology Based Standards*: The overriding considerations are not risk reduction but the cost and efficacy of a control measure (e.g. serviceability measures).

- *Risk Balancing Standards*: The balance of the benefits of risk reduction against the expected costs incurred are considered in setting risk management goals (e.g. security of supply, Section 19 (Water Act, 1989) undertakings).

Although WLC encapsulates the simple risk definition it is not a risk analysis *per se*. Of the three definitions provided above, WLC as presented within this book falls under *Technology Based Standard* (ACS, 1998) in that it deals with the cost and efficacy of interventions. It accounts for all monetary risks explicitly, with the statutory risks implied through the valuation of the associated costs. The setting of any risk based mandatory levels (e.g. leakage levels, security of supply) are outside of the Methodology. Once set, they and their associated costs can be brought into the framework. An exception to this is the water quality module. The regulation of water quality comes under the heading of *Hazard Based Standards* (ACS, 1998). In the water quality module, costs are valued based on the avoidance of those costs associated with prosecution. Part of the prosecution costs can be estimated from the magnitude of historical fines and associated legal costs.

Although the setting of appropriate levels of risk lies outside the approach, the "Decision Tool" allows the operational and maintenance decisions to be determined for the given risk scenario and allows all the monetary consequences to be quantified. Therefore, the WLC framework (through the way in which it is configured) becomes the scenario manager within an identified risk based strategy. Further details of how the Methodology can be considered within such a framework, are provided in Chapter 9.

CHAPTER TWO
Whole Life Costing

2.1   Introduction

A Whole Life Costing approach to the management of water distribution networks has the aim of achieving the lowest overall network cost consistent with meeting required standards of performance. In essence, WLC is a management tool for economic evaluation that links system performance, sometimes referred to as serviceability, to the cost consequences of that performance. By adopting an integrated approach, WLC facilitates the investigation of "what-if" scenarios and allows the evaluation of the cost effectiveness of a particular scenario. As a management tool it has the flexibility to allow decision makers to configure a problem to suit particular circumstances, either by seeking to minimise costs subject to constraints on required levels of performance or to maximise performance subject to constraints on expenditure. In order to do this the performance of water distribution networks has to be linked to expenditures.

All expenditures incurred by a water provider, whether they are termed operational (opex) or capital (capex), result from it being in existence to provide the service of a supply of water to its customers. If it did not exist then it would incur no costs (thus all costs can be said to be activity-based). The main purpose of expenditure then is to maintain or enhance system performance and serviceability to customers such that it meets the requirements of all stakeholders (customers, government, regulators, water companies). In order to optimise expenditure it is preferable to take a long term perspective so that the full effects and consequences of expenditure on performance can be properly evaluated and accounted for. Adopting a long term approach complements the fact that most water supply assets have a relatively long "useful" life. Under such circumstances, the distinction between opex and capex becomes unnecessary; they are both expenditures on the system.

In this chapter the reader is introduced, through a short review of some of the literature, to WLC and the complementary techniques of activity based costing and life cycle assessments, which underpin much of the accounting for whole life costs. The particular aspects of the general methodology that have an important bearing on the application of WLC to water distribution networks, such as geographic, temporal and cost boundaries, are discussed along with a brief introduction to discount rates and asset life. It concludes with an introduction to the conceptual framework that has been used to develop an accounting that is complementary with network performance modules.

2.2   A Literature Review

2.2.1   Whole Life Costing

Whole life costing is a term that is predominantly though not exclusively used in an engineering context, particularly civil engineering, with respect to the provision of infrastructure. As a term it has been around for nearly 20 years (Chenery, 1984) and advocated as an alternative approach to the choice and design of structures. It was noted that *"Environmental costs and those charges associated with in-service use of construction projects seldom adequately totalled with initial capital expenditure to derive an overall monetary commitment"* and *"The **whole life cost** of construction in a conventional sense should include such factors as initial construction cost, operating, maintenance and repair charges and an allowance for demolition"* (Chenery, 1984). It is also clear that there was a recognition that environmental factors also had a role to play though the emphasis was more on the physical rather than the ecological: *"it was the role of the designer to ameliorate costs in use by sensible choice of materials and structural form"*.

Even at this stage there was a divergence of terminology used, though this was more apparent than real. The Royal Institution of Chartered Surveyors were promoting at that time more conventional approaches to appraisal, life cycle cost planning (LCCP) and life cycle cost management (LCCM). Together these would give the total life cycle costs, being the total cost of a new acquisition plus the costs for the utilisation and planned maintenance of the building over the operational life. In essence these are two sides of the same coin. There is the recognition that initial capital cost represents a portion and usually a minor one, of the overall costs incurred. The responsible approach should therefore be to extend appraisals to take account of this fact. It has only been in the last couple of years that this process has taken hold, the Department of the Environment, Transport and the Regions (DETR) noted: *"Until very recently, the construction industry was preoccupied with minimising capital costs and rarely concerned itself with issues of Operation and Maintenance"* (DETR, 1998).

Whole life costing has now entered the mainstream in a number of areas of engineering, and beyond. Its application to buildings and structures has built on the early discussions already mentioned. The British Standards Institution has now issued BS/ISO 15686 Part 1 2000 Building and constructed assets – Service life planning, with Parts 2 & 3 out in draft for public comment. The Office of Government Commerce in Construction Procurement Guidance No 7 Whole Life Costs (2000) has been prepared for projects related to the construction of facilities for government use. The theme running through this and other documents prepared by various government departments and agencies is that decisions are to *"be made solely on the basis of value for money in terms of the optimum combination of whole life costs and quality to meet the user's requirements"* (OGC, 2000).

Within the buildings and structures sector a whole life costing forum has been established (http://www.wlcf.org.uk). Together with the Building Research Establishment (Centre for Whole Life Performance), a number of commercial organisations, including consultants, developers and contractors have come together to establish an information and database on whole life costs of products and services. This information is at the disposal of the members of the forum. It is intended to enable the forum members to meet rising expectations and, at the same time, enhance their position as market leaders. The work of the forum relates directly to procurement initiatives such as Best Value, Private Finance Initiative and Public Private Partnerships, Prime Contracting, all government centred or inspired.

It is therefore not surprising that the whole life costing approach is being applied to other areas of facility or infrastructure provision associated with government. These include road infrastructure and higher education.

The Higher Education Funding Council for England has taken the lead in developing and promoting whole life costing within the overall procurement strategy (HEFCE, 1998). It was recognised that the resource allocation process deals with items separately from revenue, so that the decisions to procure do not depend on the availability of funds to meet ongoing costs. As capital funds are often limited, there is pressure to minimise capital costs. The whole life costing approach adopted within HEFCE recognises that decisions should be informed by three factors;

- qualitative judgements about what really matters when considering options,
- needs of the users,
- whole life costs.

This is a framework that incorporates consultation and dialogue between all parties concerned and encourages users and others to specify usage, technical requirements, support required and lifetime.

It is of interest to note that the approach is not just about comparing the costs of alternatives but includes as an important element non-financial considerations affecting choice.

Since the late 1980s the Transport Research Laboratory (TRL) has been involved with developing the whole life costing approach to transport infrastructure, from scheme specific applications to the whole of the major road network (Wood, 2000). Whole life cost models have been developed for the assessment of construction works, maintenance management, bridges and other aspects such that alternative solutions to the design, construction and maintenance can be compared. The policy of the Highways Agency, since 1999, is that all works must be evaluated using a whole life costing approach in order to meet with government best value policy requirements. The approach has been extended to incorporate several factors (environmental) that were previously not significant or regarded as externalities.

The application of whole life costing to pipelines and water distribution networks has been more recently discussed (Herbert, 1994; Mukhopadhyay, 1994; Conroy and Hall, 1995) in the UK. In the water industry it has been suggested that whole life costing is an approach which could be applied to the rehabilitation of water mains. Mukhopadhyay (1994) stated that the costs and benefits of rehabilitation should be considered on all fronts, Herbert (1994) commented that preference should be given to solutions which implied higher construction costs but lower operating costs in order to minimise costs overall. Conroy and Hall (1995) advocated an integrated approach to rehabilitation planning and leakage control in order to reduce whole life costs. The need for an integrated approach that encompasses some of the many facets of water distribution systems has been emphasised by practitioners and researchers in this field (Edwards, 1996 and Conroy, 1997). The Water Research Centre (WRc)'s Pipeline Technology Group has been active in developing this application to pipelines though not to whole distribution systems. An approach that encapsulates an economic understanding of the whole life costs associated with the operation of distribution networks may, however, be the most economically viable for operators in the long run.

From the above it can be concluded that whole life costing is not a new approach even though it is only in the past couple of years that its application has begun to be accepted. Its adoption has been most marked in the provision of public sector infrastructure and services, a sector where ownership of the assets and responsibility for costs remain with the same organisation throughout the life of the facility, i.e. the government. Its adoption by the private sector can be less clearly demonstrated, partly due to the structural differences alluded to and partly due to the adoption of different terminology, which will be dealt with below.

The acceptance and incorporation of whole life costing has received a boost from such initiatives as PFI, PPP and Best Value approaches to procurement across a wide range of government services. This has come about because of the difficulties of raising sufficient tax revenue to meet the costs of maintaining, renewing and improving the social and economic infrastructure. Emphasis is placed on whole life costing, revenues and the risks associated with creating and operating a business and, hence, on performance over the economic life of the infrastructure provided. This has led to a fundamental shift in the nature of the public sector market, though this is not explored further here as it is not relevant.

What can be deduced from this is that a whole life costing approach appears to offer advantages to the developer/owner/operator in a number of circumstances. The general characteristics, which might not hold true in all cases nor be exhaustive, might be summarised as follows;

- the physical facility provided has a "long" lifetime,
- initial capital costs are significant,
- maintenance/operational costs equal or exceed the initial capital cost,
- the facility provides a service rather than a product,
- income stream is over the lifetime of the facility,
- there is usually a single body responsible for the facility through its lifetime.

Although whole life costing is being applied across a number of areas within what might broadly be called the engineering sector, there is relative agreement on what whole life costing is.

"Whole life costing attempts to optimise the benefits of short and long term investment." (Bayliffe).

"The whole life cost model should aim to include the total costs to the department or agency for all resources relating to the facility over its life and should include the relevant portion of costs for all internal and overhead resources." (OGC, 2000).

"Whole life costing provides the means of determining if it is cost effective to invest in a more expensive product initially to reduce costs in the long run." (DETR, 2000).

"A rationale for choice in circumstances where there are alternative means of achieving a given object, and where those alternatives differ not only in their initial costs, but also in their subsequent operational costs." (BRE, 2000).

"Whole life costing involves recognising the lifetime costs of acquiring an asset rather than simply focusing on the initial purchase price or capital cost." (JPPSG, 1996).

"A tool to assist in assessing the cost performance of construction works, aimed at facilitating choices where there are alternative means of achieving the client's objective, and where those alternatives differ not only in their initial costs but also in their subsequent operational costs." (BS/ISO 15686).

It is clear from the above that there is a broad consensus as to what whole life costing is and what it should encompass. In essence there are two components that are interrelated, one is the costs and the other is the life or lifetime of the facility. The costs include the initial capital or purchase costs required to establish the facility as well as all operational, maintenance, rehabilitation, repair costs and, where relevant, the decommissioning costs. It is also further noted that it is not just internal or direct costs that have to be considered but also overhead costs as well. When considering procurement DETR (2000a) has suggested that important elements of cost include (see also Resource Management Guidance – Procurement, DETR, 2000b);

- direct running costs,
- indirect costs – additional costs arising from inefficiencies,
- administrative costs,
- spending to save,
- recyclability,
- cost of disposal – paying a premium to reduce future costs.

A more exhaustive treatment of the range of costs that can be considered for inclusion is given by USEPA (1995).

Life time is a vaguer term and is used to indicate either economic life, operating life, design life or useful life, whichever happens to accord with the purpose and use of the facility being considered. In many cases there is no definitive term of life, as will be discussed below.

2.3   Activity Based Costing

Activity based costing (ABC) emerged as an alternative to conventional costing systems. It was developed in the USA by Harvard Business School Professors Kaplan and Cooper in the 1980s and is a process of individually listing and measuring the cost of each activity contributing to the production and delivery of a particular product or service. Activity Based Costing is a means of assigning an organisation's costs to its products and services through the activities that incur the costs. Overhead costs are traced to products and services by identifying the cost of resources required by the activities to produce the output. In the case of water supply, the unit cost of water reflects the various cost drivers of an activity and the expenditures on labour, materials, equipment and services required to produce that unit of water. It differs from

"conventional costing in its treatment of non-volume related overhead costs. Many significant overheads are related to specific activities which are relatively independent of production volume. It is the volume of such activities (not the volume of production) which consume resources and therefore determine the overhead cost.

These activities drive the overhead costs and ABC uses such activities for both production costing and process control." (Innes and Mitchell, 1990).

Activity based costing grew out of the limitations of traditional product costing and more especially out of criticisms of the way overheads were allocated. It is a more refined approach for assigning overheads to products and computing product costs. Many organisational resources exist for activities that are unrelated to physical volume; assuming that products or services consume all resources in proportion to their production volumes distorts costs. This emphasises the need to better understand the behaviour of overhead costs, what causes them and how they relate to what is being produced. In the long run most costs are not fixed but are driven by activities. Costs are incurred in order to acquire a supply of resources (e.g. labour, materials) which are then consumed by activities. The production of a product can only occur if it is created by activities and the activities cause costs to be incurred. A link is made between activities and products by assigning costs of activities to products based on an individual product's consumption or demand for each activity. With an activity based costing system cost drivers are used to relate activities to products, and there can be many different drivers.

In order to assign activity costs to products a cost driver must be selected for each activity. The driver must provide a good explanation for the costs incurred and it should be easily measurable and identifiable with the products. Cost drivers should represent a reasonably homogeneous measure of output for each activity, if not they will not provide a satisfactory explanation of the activity costs. Cost drivers have to be applied to products, so they must be measurable in such a way as to be identifiable with individual products.

By its nature ABC is most easily identifiable with process based manufacturing industries but this is not to say that it is not applicable to other sectors. Indeed, one of the factors that gave rise to its development was the failure of traditional management accounting methods to deal with overheads when these became a significant part of a firm's cost structure. In the current manufacturing environment an increasing proportion of total cost does not vary with volume of production. This is a situation that is not restricted to manufacturing but is common across many sectors. Thus the ABC approach can be applied to a wide variety of situations (Maccarrone, 1998; Sohal and Chung, 1998; Emblemsvag, 2001). ABC acknowledges that one cannot manage costs, one can only manage what is being done, i.e. activities. The merits of ABC have been discussed by several authors (Cooper, 1990; O'Guin, 1990; Brinker, 1994; Edwards, 1998) and there is a general consensus that ABC is a more accurate method of calculating product costs. Although there are no reported examples of the method being applied in the water industry there is no reason why this cannot be done. Indeed, the Ofwat RAG 4.01 Analysis of Costs by Activity can be taken as a partial application of this approach, which could be expanded to encompass all cost centres.

2.4   Life Cycle Assessment

Life cycle assessment considers the effects associated with the production, use and disposal of a product (its life cycle) on the resources and environment that supports and surrounds its production, use and disposal. Some commentators see the main purpose of LCA as identifying the environmental consequences of a product, process or activity through its entire life cycle and to identify opportunities for achieving environmental improvement. Life cycle costs are those associated with the consequences of the life cycle of a product, process or activity, in other words the cost associated with its use or abuse of resources. Environmental impacts can give rise to additional costs, which should be included in order to determine the life cycle costs.

There is debate as to what should or should not be included in life cycle costing. Some regard it as covering only private or internal costs whilst others include both internal and external costs. What is included depends on the purpose for which the methodology is being used.

Some practitioners apply the same methodology to the products, processes or activities that provide the input services and outputs of each of the stages. In other words the envelope of what is included expands. A practical problem then arises as it becomes difficult to decide how far up and down the supply chain to apply this and still keep LCA tractable, sensible and useful. Taken to the extreme the whole of the output of the world's industrial system would have to be accounted for in any application, a situation that is clearly impractical. In view of the difficulties a first step is to confine the methodology to the directly attributable environmental consequences of process activities and not for the inputs goods and services.

Life cycle assessment is one of a number of other terms and approaches that have been applied outside of infrastructure or public sector service provision. A reading of the management and environmental accounting literature would suggest that such terminologies and approaches originate mainly from the manufacturing or industry based sectors and indeed the influence of environmental accounting has been marked. A booklet produced by the United States Environmental Protection Agency provides a good introduction to many of the key concepts and terms that are in use (USEPA, 1995). The concept that comes closest to the whole life cost approach espoused by engineers is the life cycle framework. Interestingly, this approach is incorporated as a key part of the ISO 14000 Environmental Management Series, and ISO 14040–14042 deals specifically with life cycle assessment. Life cycle terms include: life cycle design, life cycle assessment, life cycle analysis, life cycle cost assessment, life cycle accounting and life cycle cost. Life cycle cost has been defined as *"the amortised annual cost of a product, including capital costs, installation costs, operating costs, maintenance costs, and disposal costs discounted over the lifetime of a product"* (USEPA, 1995).

The similarity between the two sets of terms is noteworthy and the difference perhaps has more to do with divergent background and traditions than actual substance. Although there is a growing recognition that the life cycle framework can be incorporated into the whole life costing approach (BRE, 2000). One reason for this is that the life cycle framework is *"a reasonably well-established method to measure the environmental burden of products and/or materials"*, though it is not without its problems (DETR, 2001). Life cycle "thinking" is emerging as a major tool for environmental evaluation and management, something that has been borne out by surveys of large industrial corporations (Heiskanen, 2000). Use of life cycle framework is a means to find out the cost drivers and causes for various cost components contributing over the lifetime of a product or facility. It helps with the identification of environmental and other costs that are often hidden within overheads (Bullinger et al., 1996) or not taken account of at all as they are regarded as future costs and therefore do not need to be included in any evaluation or analysis.

Within manufacturing there is an emphasis on using life cycle analyses in the early stages of the design process as *"during the first 20% of the design process 80% or more of the manufacturing costs and product attributes are decided"* (McAloone and Evans, 1996). In the case of water distribution networks the systems are already in being. However, as they are constantly being worked on there are opportunities to optimise both the design of rehabilitated works and their operation. So it can be seen that whole life costing, incorporating life cycle approaches, can combine elements of life cycle design and life cycle costs within its overall framework.

Even though most applications of life cycle framework include elements of environmental cost, there is scope for confusion. Most view life cycle costing as referring only to private costs, as previously illustrated, and not societal costs (USEPA, 1995). The DETR has adopted a slightly different approach to the treatment of public (societal and environmental) costs. There is a need to identify green issues and ensure that these are considered in the procurement process (DETR, 2000a), *"the impact of the facility on the external environment needs to address the direct impact on the individuals who live and work in the vicinity of the facility. We also need to address the global environment"* (OGC, 2000). It also has to be noted that the European Commission has issued a draft communication regarding the scope for taking account of environmental matters in procurement. With respect to government procurement, wider costs (e.g. costs of congestion or long term pollution on local communities) outside of those that are directly paid for must not be considered at the evaluation stage as part of a financial analysis. However, these wider aspects can be considered at specification stage, meaning;

- the cost of acquiring new landfill sites caused by waste paper generation cannot be factored into a cost analysis, but it can be addressed through specifying measures to reduce waste,

- the cost of treating pollution-related diseases can be addressed by specifying more efficient cleaner vehicles.

But relative environmental aspects, as part of a non-financial qualitative assessment, can be taken into account (DETR, 2000a). DETR is currently funding work on the estimation of impacts of building components in order to provide information for decision making on the basis of environmental and economic impact (BRE, 2000).

So clearly the impetus and requirement to include societal considerations within a whole life costing framework is already with us.

However, it would be misleading to assume from the foregoing review that there are no attendant problems associated with the application of whole life costing. These have been identified by several authors. Because of the nature of the method the information required for its implementation is spread across a wide area of operations and disciplines *"considering any variable affects many parts of a business and raises many strategic issues"* (Evans and McAloone). This has implications for access to the required information, gathering it together and its interpretation. There is a need for a multi-disciplinary approach and this in itself can create logistical difficulties. Acting against this has been the trend towards greater out-sourcing and diffusion of responsibility for products and processes, it becomes so diffuse among economic factors that it dissolves completely (Beck, 1992 and Jamieson, 1992). If there is a lesser degree of responsibility and by implication, accountability, the proper application and acceptance of whole life costing and its consequences becomes more problematic. However, countering this has been the observation that the approach directs attention, and potential action, to new issues and introduces managers to new perspectives beyond the traditional scope of business environmental management (Welford, 1995 and Heiskanen, 2000). Also because of the nature of the approach it seeks to link together activities, some of which may be occurring in different organisations, implying that it could be influential outside of the organisation applying it (Heiskanen, 2000).

But this leads onto another problem that has already been touched on. What are the limits and boundaries for the application of the framework? The complexity of a full assessment and costing would involve many materials, parts, players and processes. As the scope of an assessment broadens so the cost of data collection and the attendant uncertainties increase significantly (Schaltegger, 1997). There would appear to be no consensus on how to determine what the boundaries or scope should be. Indeed, Schaltegger (1997) concludes that *"an 'ideal' LCA is not feasible in practice"*. A common approach is to consider only those costs that the operator/owner is responsible for whilst at the same time giving qualitative consideration to broader issues (e.g. societal) involved (DETR, 2000).

Within the manufacturing sector there is a preference for site rather than product specific LCAs to be carried out. This avoids the obvious problems of aggregation, especially of environmental aspects with different spatial dimensions. It is an approach that is easier to apply and has been supported to some extent by the introduction and acceptance of the Eco-management and Audit Scheme (EMAS) and ISO 14000 accreditation (Schaltegger, 1997).

Even with such an approach there still remains the problem of reconciling different classes of environmental burdens in such a way as to be able to make meaningful comparisons. The inclusion of qualitative evaluation is a way of overcoming this difficulty but it has been seen as lacking the rigour of quantitative comparison. Indeed, it has been noted that the inability to reduce whole life costs to a single metric in a neutral, objective and scientific manner that would command universal acceptance (DETR, 2001) is seen as a major difficulty.

In what is more and more a competitive environment there will be an obvious reluctance on the part of some to apply a WLC approach if this is seen to increase costs and reduce competitive edge. Unless there is a threat of legislation or regulation and unless the cost can be balanced with a benefit, no organisation is going to be proactive in this area. There has to be a clear perception that the application of a WLC approach will be economic for the organisation concerned (Bostock, 1996 and McAloone and Evans, 1996). To encourage this strong incentives should be introduced (Schaltegger, 1997). Though what these might be has not been specified, it is clear that the initiatives by the British government such as its *greening government* policies, procurement guidance and EC directives are moving in this direction. The scope for its application beyond government in the regulated market of the privatised public utility sector is certainly evident and there are indications that it might gain acceptance (Ofwat, 2000a), however, much work still needs to be done.

Apart from its application, two other areas are of concern, the selection of a representative life for appraisal and the selection of a discount rate, though they are little discussed. It can be noted from the various articles that deal with whole life or life cycle costing that the term lifetime is used but seldom defined. Indeed, there is a proliferation of terms used which would tend to suggest that there is no common understanding as to what is meant in practice. This probably reflects that there is no unique period of time, most facilities being an amalgam of components having differing properties, each of which might have a certain useful life dependent on the circumstances in which it is employed. *"Misgivings were expressed over the difficulty in selecting a representative life for which to exercise any appraisal. The allocation of life could be more precisely defined for mechanical plant which tend to age more predictably."* (Chenery, 1984). The choice of life span or period of appraisal would appear to be a matter of informed choice. In its approach the Whole Life Costing Forum (WLCF) emphasise that *"the required life of the whole asset must be agreed with the client"*. A practical and not unreasonable approach, given the consulting/contracting background of the majority of those involved in the Forum.

Discount rates are another area of uncertainty, influenced as they are by a range of factors. It is interesting to note that the WLCF does not discuss this point. A separate section will be devoted to a discussion of discount rates as it has an important influence on the outcome of any appraisal. *"Detailed discussion ensued on the derivation of discount rates to be employed in life cycle calculations. One contributor felt that discount rates tended to be higher since they were linked to investment appraisal, where an emphasis on lower rates would enhance the maintenance value of the equation. Inevitably, selection was influenced by political factors."* (Chenery, 1984). It would appear that not much has changed in the intervening 20 odd years.

2.5   General Methodology

The accounting for whole life costs provides a methodology whereby the costs arising from the operation, maintenance and management of a water distribution network can be calculated and coupled to the performance of the network. It links the performance of the system and management decisions regarding operation enabling the consequences of decisions to be evaluated in monetary terms. Alternatively, the impact of a management decision can be linked to changes in network performance. The key to this is the determination of costs associated with each cost driver. A cost driver is a quantity that when combined with a unit cost gives a total cost of an activity. The quantity results from the volume or intensity of an activity. Activities are undertaken in order to provide a required service and this requires a flow of resources which incurs costs. Thus cost drivers indicate how the flow of resources (and costs) change with the intensity of activity. They use a physical measure of activity which best represents the driving forces. Unit costs can be derived from historical cost and performance data available to the operator.

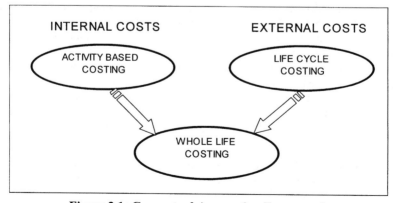

Figure 2.1: Conceptual Accounting Framework

Whole-life costing uses both ABC and LCA as a means of determining all the costs over the whole life of a network (Figure 2.1). Emphasis is usually on the inclusion and accounting for direct costs associated with water supply operations though this framework goes beyond that in order to take a more holistic approach. Whole life costing is a relatively new concept, especially with regard to its operationalisation and implementation. Aspects such as how to treat costs and expenditures other than the direct costs are little explored in existing literature. There is no consensus as to what might or might not be included though there are references to the need to consider the environment. The whole life costing developed here includes all expenditures.

Such an analysis is not carried out at one point in time considering the stream of costs over the whole of the useful life of the water distribution network. It goes beyond useful life where there are consequences or contingent liabilities that remain even after cessation of activity – decommissioning costs.

2.6   Cost Identification

Whole life costing can be defined as encompassing all the costs (private as well as public) that accrue to the initiation, provision, operation, maintenance, servicing and decommissioning, over the useful life of a service infrastructure. Its application to distribution network management aims to achieve the lowest network service provision operating cost, when all costs are considered, whilst meeting statutory standards and regulatory performance. It is therefore necessary to be able to identify cost drivers and via unit costs determine the total cost consequent on performance.

Costs are either private or public. Private costs are those that accrue to the operator from being in the business of providing a service to customers. They include costs that might conventionally be termed direct, indirect or hidden and they include both operational and capital expenditures. Public costs are those that accrue to society as a result of the operator being in business but that the operator, currently, does not have to account for. They are sometimes referred to as social and environmental or societal costs. The accounting methodology adopted considers both of these categories of costs and seeks to attribute them to unique performance drivers. All costs are directly attributed to the actions or operations that give rise to them.

Thus, there are no overhead or general cost items, these are all driven by operational activities. In the same way there are no absolute fixed costs. There may be some activities whose costs do not change with volume of production. In other words, the volume of the activity is driven by a different set of parameters to the volume of production of the final product (water). However, under a different set of conditions such a cost item would change. For example, if the size and number of customers served by an organisation were to double then the size of the call centre, and hence the magnitude of cost, would change, all other things being equal. Hence, it could be that the size–cost relationship would be a stepwise function and that many other of the *"fixed costs"* can be treated in a similar fashion. Pragmatically though there may not be sufficient information available to enable all fixed costs to be converted to variable costs. Therefore what is proposed is not a true ABC system but rather a practical attempt to implement the principles as far as the available information allows.

By treating all costs as *variable* with respect to a cost driver it should be possible to relate the cost of an activity to the volume of that activity. It is both operational and capital expenditures (referred to as *opex* and *capex*) that are of interest. Opex covers the costs of routine operation, maintenance, repair, minor works and other activities required to enable a water system to function. This does not imply anything about the adequacy or quality of service provided by the system so it also covers non-routine operations, such as leakage and bursts and the expenditures associated with them.

Capital expenditure in a distribution network can be of two kinds. It can be to provide for network extension and it can be investment in the existing infrastructure. In this instance the investment goes beyond routine maintenance and repair focussing on aspects such as rehabilitation (upgrading or replacement). The aim of both capex and opex is the same, to allow the network to perform in an acceptable manner. As such they are treated as complementary and interlinked.

Expenditure on base service provision is required to maintain the current level of serviceability to customers, whilst enhancement is where there is a permanent increase in the current level of serviceability to a new "base" level. Expenditure on enhancement is divided into quality enhancements, enhanced service level and supply/demand balance. Each of these links with a change in level of service.

The accounting framework developed herein extends the traditional practice of accounting for private costs to include external or public costs that are consequent on the operation of a system. It therefore takes a more holistic view on what can be included and accounted for. In doing so it allows the user to anticipate potential regulatory requirements, to internalise some externalities and evaluate the effect of this as part of a decision making process.

2.7   Boundaries

Water distribution networks exist within a set of boundaries and in applying WLC these have to be considered and explicitly defined as they have a determining influence on the results of any analysis. Therefore a proper appreciation of them is required in order that meaningful and informative results are obtained that will aid decision making. Three sets of boundaries are recognised: geographical, temporal and cost. Each of these is discussed in the following sections. Geographical boundaries define the extent of the network considered and this has a bearing on the assets considered and their performance over time. Definition of the spatial boundaries also holds implications for costs, the two are closely linked. Temporal boundaries determine the time horizon for any analysis. When considering operation costs this can have a significant impact on the total costs incurred. What costs are considered and included is a consequence of and flows from the other two sets of boundaries. It is also a question of the extent to which costs other than direct costs are recognised and accounted for and what at-boundary on-costs should be included.

2.7.1   Geographic Boundaries

Water service providers normally have a functional hierarchy of their water supply systems (assets) that is geographically based. These are integrated systems that treat and transport water from source to consumer and return the wastewater from consumer to the environment. A distribution network is one part of the integrated systems. Water distribution networks consist largely of underground assets and can be characterised as being everything downstream of water service reservoirs and upstream of the point of first practical use by the consumer (the consumer's tap). For the purpose of applying WLC this boundary needs to be further defined and a decision made as to how much of the distribution network should be subject to WLC analysis. Such a decision has implications not only with respect to performance but also for the cost accounting framework. The basic unit of operational management of water distribution networks, the lowest level of aggregation of assets, is commonly referred to as a District Meter Area (DMA) in the UK. There are further levels of aggregation until they are all brought together as the water service providers' assets. The numbers of levels of aggregation reflect the water service providers' management and operation of network assets and the influence of geographical and physical realities. Figure 2.2 provides the typical hierarchical structure observed in the water supply systems of England and Wales.

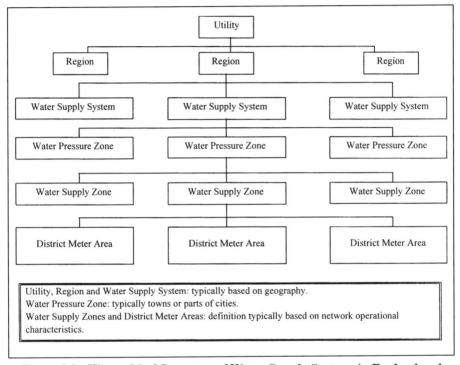

Figure 2.2: Hierarchical Structure of Water Supply Systems in England and Wales

In applying WLC to water distribution networks a number of factors have to be balanced when considering the choice of appropriate geographical boundaries. These relate to the nature of the underground assets on the one hand and to the characterisation and allocation of costs on the other. The geographical boundaries or level of aggregation of assets chosen should adequately reflect in their characteristics a degree of homogeneity of performance and location. The choice should not introduce too great a degree of complexity but nor should it be so general as not to offer an insight into the peculiar characteristics present. In other words the choice should meet the criteria of; is it reasonable and meaningful to use such boundaries? On the cost side the boundaries chosen should be informed by the water service provider's management cost accounting framework and especially the manner in which costs could be allocated. The ability to apply a geographically differentiated ABC approach may have a determining influence on the choice of boundaries within which it is possible to apply the WLC. It should allow the variations in distribution network characteristics and costs across a water service providers sphere of operations to be accounted for. It should not, however, introduce an unnecessary informational and computational burden.

In the approach developed herein it is suggested that an appropriate level of aggregation would be what has been referred to as a water supply zone (WSZ), consisting of a collection of DMAs.

2.7.2   Cost Boundaries

A water distribution network does not exist in isolation, it is an interlinked part of a water supply system. How a water distribution network is operated and performs can affect systems both upstream (abstraction, treatment and transfer) and downstream (wastewater collection, treatment and disposal). The costs to be accounted for are those that are driven by the activities that occur within chosen water distribution network boundaries. However, given that the cost of treated water is dependent on the upstream system, the interconnected nature of costs should be explicitly included in the accounting framework. This represents an at-boundary on-cost that needs to be reflected and included. Ideally, a comprehensive WLC could be expanded to include and interrelate upstream performance and costs. This however is still to be developed. Impacts on downstream performance and costs are not considered. Within these boundaries there needs to be some consideration given as to the range of costs that should be included and accounted for. Ideally both private and public costs associated with the operation and maintenance of a water distribution network should be accounted for and all private costs should be included.

Costs can be broken down into three basic functional categories: labour related costs, materials and equipment, and services. This does not indicate where these expenditures originate, how they are represented and how they are tracked. There are two aspects that reflect the nature of the service provided. One relates to the activities required to provide the service and the other is the geographical dimension of those activities. An activity, which involves costs, takes place in a set location and this might fall within or outside the geographical boundaries set. However, the reason for the activity occurring is related to what is going on within the geographical boundaries of a distribution network. This applies to costs that might be termed overheads or general items. These costs need to be related back to the network and accounted for, as has previously been discussed, a principle that underlies the application of ABC. For example, a burst might give rise to a complaint. The complaint is received by a "call centre" which then passes it on to a network controller. The network controller reviews the developing situation and initiates action, an investigation perhaps. As a result of the burst, various reports are generated, some of which are passed through to the regulators. As a result of the occurrence of an incident within part of a distribution network various activities have taken place. The activities have been driven by the incident and hence the costs.

2.7.3   Temporal Boundaries

As WLC considers all costs over the useful life for the infrastructure there is a need to understand what is meant by the term "useful life" and how long it might be. In the context of water distribution networks the concept of the *"useful life"* or *"asset life"* can be problematic. The individual assets that make up the system (e.g. pipes and fittings) may have finite useful lives when their role in a network is considered. An asset may have a recommended technical service or design life but this may be affected by other factors that can impact on its useful life. However, a distribution network is made up of a collection of individual assets each of differing materials, specification and locations and each with different service histories. The processes of operation, maintenance and repair required to provide a service to consumers continually changes the characteristics of individual components and hence the system. The *useful life* of components changes as does that of the system and this can be very long, hundreds of years perhaps. Useful or asset life becomes something that is indeterminate. The "useful life" is constantly being altered by the way in which a water service provider operates and maintains a network and in turn, this will affect performance. It is recognised that assets that are well maintained and looked after will "last longer" than assets that are not "well maintained". In other words benign interventions can extend the life of an item. Thus while the idea of a useful life for an individual component may have some basis in reality when it is factored up to the level of a water distribution network it becomes a great deal more obscure. It is open to question whether the concept of useful life can be applied to a system that provides a service, when even if a particular component fails it is still able to continue to provide a service.

The primary purpose of expenditure on distribution networks is to maintain system performance and serviceability to customers rather than a single asset's performance. So, within a whole life costing approach to distribution networks, a period of analysis has to be determined that is long enough for the effects of expenditures on performance to be manifest through the system but not so long as to trivialise them when discounted. Period of analysis therefore takes over from the "useful" life, depreciation period or accounting lifespan as a more realistic and pragmatic approach. In our work we have adopted a period of 50 years.

Water distribution networks are not only composed of a large number of individual assets but there is also generally a deliberate policy of intervention. Interventions are usually to ensure that the system is capable of delivering a service to customers that meets some set of performance requirements. So, the state of the network is different after an intervention to what it was before and this will have affected its "life". It may be impossible to be able to quantify what the impact on the "life" of the system has been, even if we were able to agree which "life" was referred to. A water distribution network does not have a life in the same way that a living organism does, that at some point it ceases to exist as an entity.

What is of relevance though within WLC is period of analysis. The whole life costing is a means of evaluating costs and performance of a distribution network over time and of comparing how these differ depending on the decisions taken. What then would be a reasonable period of analysis that allows the full effects of management decisions and environmental effects to become manifest and therefore accounted for without introducing unrealistic demands on the analysis? It should be long enough for all the costs and consequences to be included such that no one option would be favoured over another. A potential complication lies in the differing demands and the time periods over which the consequences of actions become manifest between man-made and natural systems. Natural systems tend to respond on a longer timescale. However, adopting very long term timescales for the evaluation of a distribution system might seem too altruistic and increases the margin of error and uncertainty.

The choice of a period of analysis becomes a pragmatic one made in consultation with all major parties involved. Also of importance in deciding the period of analysis is the choice of discount rate to be used in the analysis. A high discount rate has the effect of decreasing significantly future expenditures and so there is little point in adopting a long period of analysis, for example increasing the discount rate from 2 to 4% approximately halves the time needed to reduce an investment by half. Moving from 4 to 8% approximately halves the time again. It is suggested that the period of analysis should not be shorter than 40 years with a maximum of 100 years for practical reasons. A reasonable period of analysis of 50 years is suggested as a starting point.

2.8   External Costs

Each action performed to maintain a distribution network in operation will result in some impact on the environment, whether this is the social, economic, political or ecological environment.   Under most prevailing free market conditions, the consequences and costs arising from such actions are not directly carried by the operator but rather by the environment in its broadest sense. These are sometimes referred to as "externalities" and are not included in conventional cost accounting systems. Recognising the perverse effects of some externalities, there has been a tendency to introduce measures that seek to internalise part or all of the external costs. It is recommended that consideration should be given to their inclusion in order to ensure that all relevant costs (social and environmental) are accounted for. There are difficulties in calculating external costs and some of these are addressed in Chapter 3.

2.9   Discount Rates

The application of the cost accounting framework will lead to the generation of an expenditure profile over the period of analysis adopted. When there is a need to compare alternative uses of available funds some common method of comparison is required. This is especially important if the streams of expenditures are different over time. Whole life costing, in common with a number of other techniques (e.g. cost–benefit analysis), uses a discount rate to achieve this. The discount rate chosen can have an enormous impact on the results, especially if the period of analysis is long. High discount rates favour short term improvements over long term investments. Ideally, the discount rate chosen should reflect the operator's time value of money (sometimes called *consumption discount rate*). If an economy is experiencing a growth in income and consumption through time then an additional unit of consumption will be worth less in the future than now.

Analysis has shown that there is no one correct rate of discount;

"The discount rate is not something we measure it is something we choose." (Heal, 1981).

"The principles and practice of discounting are very controversial, with many fundamental and largely unresolved theoretical controversies. In addition, a whole set of 'practical' problems exist that are very difficult to resolve satisfactorily." (Perman, Ma and McGilvray, 1996).

Economists have generally advocated setting the social discount rate at the level of long term interest rate on government bonds, plus a risk premium where appropriate. Some of the more common approaches have been to equate the discount rate with the cost of borrowing – often used in the public sector, or to use the cost of capital which sets the discount rate equal to a rate of return that covers the cost of borrowed funds plus a return on equity for shareholders – commonly used in the private sector.

Another alternative would be the opportunity cost, in other words the interest rate on other investment alternatives. A recent survey of municipal authorities in the USA found that all of these are used and that there is little overall consistency in their choice (Arditi and Messiha, 1999), though most used either cost of borrowing or cost of capital.

The argument that the market rate of interest or return on capital might be a basis on which to choose a discount rate is at first sight attractive. But it depends on a set of conditions that are difficult to meet in practice. It depends on the assumption of a perfectly competitive market economy in which no market failures exist, which is highly unlikely. It has been argued that there exists a difference between individual or private rate of time preference and public rate of time preference. So that in considering projects with substantial social future consumption benefits, a lower discount rate should be adopted rather than that used in the private markets.

It is especially difficult to resolve the choice of discount rate when long term comparisons are being made. A number of writers argue that market based discount rates are inappropriate as the market only takes account of the consumption preferences of the current generation. Individuals with finite horizons are likely to behave differently from a society that expects to remain in existence for a very long time. It is this distinction that gives rise to some of the inherent tensions associated with discounting. Frank Ramsey (1928) observed discounting to be *"ethically indefensible and arises from a weakness of imagination"*.

Projecting inflation adds a further level of complexity, especially as it is generally applied in an effort to increase accuracy of prediction, rather than aid comparison. The way inflation is treated can dramatically alter the outcome of any assessment. Although it is a reality it is more comfortable to work in constant value terms.

It is an exercise in futility to search for clear and common guidelines that will produce precise values of discount and inflation rates. In the late 1960s the US Joint Economic Committee of Congress concluded that for the public sector the opportunity cost of displaced private spending should serve to define the discount rate. There is support for this approach by US agencies, who tend to use "the real interest rate" defined as the interest rate on long term government securities less the inflation rate.

So in the end it becomes a matter of individual choice. The rate should not be chosen so that it unduly privileges one set of options over another. Nor should it be so low as to be unrealistic. A sensible approach would be to adopt a mid range estimate and to carry out sensitivity analyses to investigate the impact of the choice of discount rate on the outcome of comparisons. Noting that the current UK Treasury discount rate is 6%,[1] this would be a reasonable starting point for comparisons in the absence of any alternative figure.

2.10   Conceptual Framework of Operational Activities

The economic regulator in England and Wales, Ofwat recognises two functions in the supply of water and four for the running of the business (RAG 3.04, Reporting Guidelines, Ofwat 1999).

---

[1] The discount rate was set in 1987, as of the end of 2001 this was being re-evaluated and may fall to 5%.

SERVICE ACTIVITY	FUNCTIONS
Water Supply	Resource and Treatment
	Distribution
Business Activities	Customer Service
	Scientific Service
	Cost of Regulation
	General and Support Activities

RAG 4.01, Analysis of Operating Costs and Assets, gives a detailed outline and description of the items that are to be included under each of these functions. This breakdown of expenditures has been adopted herein for the purpose of applying WLC to water distribution networks. Figure 2.3 illustrates the sequencing of activities involved in water supply and the cost items associated with them. Business activities provide an overarching support for these activities and thus sit alongside them.

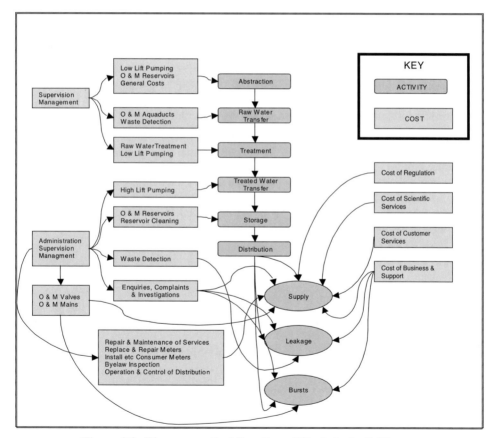

Figure 2.3: Diagrammatic Allocation of Costs to Activities

2.10.1 Capital Maintenance Activities

Capital maintenance activities can provide for the maintenance of a base or an enhanced level of performance within a distribution network. Programmes of such activities may well form part of an operator's asset management plan, which may or may not have to be agreed with a regulator, as is the case in England and Wales. Capital maintenance programmes (rehabilitation) may be targeted at improving water quality, reducing leakage, replacement of ageing mains or some other objectives. Whatever the reason, they are planned activities rather than being associated with a response to an unplanned event such as a burst – which would fall under an operational activity. The choice of rehabilitation technique ranges from replacement through to different forms of structural upgrading such as relining. The WLC approach would allow an analysis of the impact of particular capital maintenance on performance and hence on costs because of the integrated nature of the approach. The approach also would allow the investigation of the optimal extent and timing of different rehabilitation strategies, and whether individual assets should be targeted through to wholesale replacement of assets in a district.

As with operational activities, it is important to identify the relevant Business Activities, their scale and the costs associated with any particular capital maintenance activity. It would also include any external costs that might be considered relevant.

CHAPTER THREE
Environmental Aspects

3.1   Introduction

The purpose of this chapter is to outline the social and environmental aspects associated with the operation of water distribution networks and to indicate some of the implications of incorporating them into the decision making process. A feature of the approach outlined is that it does not just consider the social and environmental aspects of distribution network itself. It also considers the aspects associated with activities other than those directly associated with operation and maintenance. Thus the consideration of social and environmental aspects is expanded to cover activities such as the provision of scientific services, the facilities used, the functioning of accommodation and the services employed. A practical problem with this is the need to be clear and rational about where to draw the boundaries around social and environmental aspects – otherwise such an analysis would get out of hand and become intractable. Associated with this is the problem of the availability and usefulness of information required to undertake such analysis. Each case needs to be looked at on its merits, taking into account the scope of the work, the availability of information with the judicious application of sound judgement. What this chapter is not is a detailed guide to environmental impact assessments, cost–benefit analysis or environmental valuation. For this the reader is encouraged to explore the available literature on each of these topics.

The operation of a water distribution network, which includes work required to maintain performance over time, will interact with the milieu in which it is located. It will affect and be affected by that environment, some of which can be described in terms of cost. Costs will be incurred by the operator (private costs) because of the interaction between an activity and the environment – internalising the externality. In other cases, the operator does not have to account for the affect or the cost of the affect, it has no direct impact on operations and can be termed an externality, the costs of which are borne by the wider community. An externality comes about when the production or consumption decisions of one agent affect the utility of another in an unintended way, and no compensation is made by the producer of the external effect to the affected party. It is a complex problem to assess and assign costs to externalities. Hence, the years of debate and volume of academic articles on the subject (Loomis, 2000 and Arrow et al., 1993).

For these purposes the term *"Environment"* is used in a holistic sense. It includes such aspects as the physical, ecological, social, economic, cultural, legal and technical that together make up environment. It is important that these are recognised because ideally the way a network is operated should meet the following criteria, it should be;

- efficient and effective when all private, social and environmental costs are taken into account,
- equitable in the way different groups are affected,
- sustainable and in the interests of future generations.

Concentration on just private costs can lead to sub-optimal solutions, hence the need to adopt a holistic approach.

The impacts or externalities that might arise in the case of the operation and maintenance of a water distribution system are first discussed. This involves a detailed consideration of the processes that underpin the transport of water to consumers – what might be thought of as the life cycle of water as a product being manufactured from raw materials, commodified and delivered to the consumer as well as the various product support functions. Almost inevitably there will be waste and breakdowns in the production process, which take the form of bursts and leakage. These too produce their own social and environmental impacts and have to be added to the costs of the product. A starting point for the identification and consideration of the social and environmental impacts is outlined. Finally, there is a short section on the available valuation techniques.

3.2   Impact Assessment

The first step is to seek to identify, throughout the life cycle of the distribution system, what actions taken will cause impacts and on what. What follows is just one generalised way of approaching this problem. Other approaches may be preferred but the principal aim is to identify and quantify the range of social and environmental impacts and the way they are influenced by changes in the operation and maintenance of the distribution system. This can then be used as a starting point from which to identify any cost implications.

A matrix based approach has been used that considers which environmental characteristic would be affected by or impacted upon by an operational situation. Three broad operational situations have been identified; *normal network operation, bursts and leakage,* and *rehabilitation.* Within each of the operational situations there are a range of activities which are required to make the system function. The activities are grouped together under the main headings of Water Supply, Water Distribution, Sewage Treatment, Sludge Disposal and Business Activities.

The environmental characteristics have been broken down into; Physical Characteristics, Ecological Characteristics, Land Use and Character, Socio-economics, Infrastructure Services and Environmental Pollution. Within each one of these there are a number of sub groupings each made up of individual characteristics. In this way the range of environmental characteristics specific to the distribution of water and the way in which activities impact on the environmental characteristics can be represented. Only the primary impacts are considered and not the secondary impacts arising from an activity. For example, leakage gives rise to high levels of raw water abstraction but it is the abstraction that affects directly the resources not the leakage.

The environment is of value to society as a whole because of the contribution it makes to human welfare. The total value of environmental characteristics is a function of the total economic value of an environmental resource and the primary value of underlying ecological functions (Haywood et al., 1995) and this in turn is a function of its use value and non-use value. Use value comprises; direct and indirect use (value of benefits from ecosystem), option value (value of safeguarding the option to use) and quasi-option value (potential but unknown value of a resource). Non-use value comprises; bequest value (value to you from which others might benefit in the future) and existence value (Pearce and Moran, 1994). It is of course easier to identify the components that contribute to value than to actually value them. The primary reason for this is that markets do not exist for them, thus transactions do not occur and we cannot establish in the same way that direct use of a resource generates value.

Societal costs have to be inferred by other means and these may not capture all of the potential value. The means by which environmental values can be determined has been the subject of much research in environmental and ecological economics (Freeman, 1993; Bromley, 1995; Braden and Kolstad, 1991) and although techniques have been evolved there is still much debate surrounding their use. The methods proposed are complex and time consuming to apply and as a result there are few complete studies available. Most methods seek to establish willingness-to-pay for a certain state of the environment and then scale this up by the affected number of consumers. The assignment of value in money terms has many difficulties and so a degree of caution has to be exercised.

In the following sections the impacts of the various activities on environmental characteristics are briefly discussed in order to identify whether there are cost implications. These costs should be quantified through analysis of expenditures or other valuation techniques identified in the final section of the chapter.

3.2.1 Normal Operation

A water distribution network cannot exist in isolation, it is part of an upstream system of sources, treatment works, transfer infrastructure and storage as well as a downstream waste collection, transfer, treatment and disposal network. By its existence it creates the need for the rest of the infrastructure as well as supporting infrastructure such as electricity supplies and transportation. By creating the need for water supplies to pass through the system to the consumer, for it to be treated and made wholesome, the need for the infrastructural services required to deliver these functions is created.

By its operation a water distribution network will have environmental impacts; on air, land, water, solid and liquid waste. These impact on the assimilative capacities of the components of the environment and on the functioning of the ecological communities that use the environment as a resource. Such impacts can be minimised using technologies that reduce, remove or prevent such pollution (defensive expenditures). The imposition of progressively stricter standards through EU and national legislation is one way in which operators are being required to internalise previously external costs, realising that otherwise the costs to society outweigh any private or social benefit.

3.2.2 Water Supply

Abstraction of water, whether from groundwater, rivers or dam basins, alters the natural availability of water and has a direct impact on the physical and ecological characteristics of the environment. Abstraction patterns are variable, determined by factors such as consumer demand often running counter to natural variations. The alterations of flows have an impact on hydrological and biodiversity functions. Abstraction pumping produces emissions, usually indirectly through the use of generated electricity. Emissions (steam, SO_2, NOX, particulates and others) contribute directly to global warming and climate change. Raw water treatment has similar impacts as it is also a significant consumer of energy. The handling and use of chemicals for water treatment has the potential to cause water and land pollution (secondary impacts arising from their manufacture and transport might be included in a full life cycle analysis). The presence of raw water treatment and storage facilities has an effect on welfare aspects (employment, adequacy and reliability of supply, land use, threats to health).

The impacts on the physical environments and biodiversity will be borne by society. At present the English and Welsh Environment Agency does not seek to place an economic resource value on the use of water as its charges only cover the EA's operating cost of administration. Indirect use value relates to the supply of environmental services such as groundwater providing water to streams or the assimilative capacity of streams and rivers, which maintain a healthy environment.

An alternative approach to that of estimating willingness-to-pay could be based on estimates of the costs involved in returning the used volumes of water back to the point of abstraction. This can be thought of as defensive or avoidance costs, the costs that would be incurred in order to avoid causing an impact. Although this would not capture all the potential value of the total environmental value outline it would provide an approximation that is more readily estimated. The other potential impacts such as emissions and risk of pollution are societal and environmental costs (avoidance cost approaches may be appropriate here). The costs of waste management and especially control of solid waste may become internalised through stricter guidelines governing its generation and handling (Duty of Care for waste producers, European Packaging Directives, future legislation on producer responsibility and Integrated Product Policy).

In contrast to these negative impacts, the presence and functioning of a raw water treatment facility has beneficial effects. There can be little doubt that the provision of raw water treatment facilities has contributed to human welfare and that the contribution is greater than the cost of the service. The provision of wholesome water promotes good public health and thus avoids other costs such as loss of productivity, greater morbidity, higher healthcare costs. It provides employment and reliability and adequacy of supply. Water storage in impounding reservoirs and lakes provides amenities for communities as well as recreational facilities and a diversity of wildlife habitats.

3.2.3 Water Distribution

Water distribution has minimal direct affect on the physical and ecological environment though potentially a more significant affect on the socio-economic and infrastructure environments. The presence of a water distribution network provides employment and helps to maintain the welfare of the population served. The welfare effects go beyond aspects such as income and employment. The benefits of these can best be gauged by estimating the likely effects if they were absent. There would be severe social costs such as losses through poorer public health and increased expenditure required for social services. All these would be costs that would be carried by society as a whole, with the burden being spread disproportionally through the population. Higher levels of social welfare reflect the added value to society that arises from the provision of an infrastructure service such as water. Whilst the cost of the provision of the infrastructure service can be estimated with a degree of accuracy it is greatly more difficult to estimate the added value.

3.2.4   Business Activities

On first examination it might seem like Business Support Activities have little or no environmental impacts. However, decisions and activities undertaken by business support have a direct impact primarily on socio-economic and infrastructure services as well as environmental pollution. Services are provided that have a direct impact on aspects such as public confidence, support to customer, special interests and educational groups. They also have a direct effect on accessibility as well as recreational utilisation and conservation of assets. Managerial practices, codes of conduct, supervision, financial climate will have a major impact on the way assets are operated and maintained, which in turn determines the extent and severity of their impact on the various environmental characteristics. They have a determining influence on aspects such as choice of technology employed, attitude towards legal and regulatory compliance as well as the ethos of the organisation (e.g. how does management view the environment).

The majority of business activity costs can be categorised as internal or private costs to the organisation, some already internalised, such as the support to the various groups. Others will be much more difficult to quantify in any objective manner. It would be almost impossible, for example, to estimate what financial difference the attitude of management towards the environment makes in the day to day operation of the organisation. The last aspect is that associated with environmental pollution; the choice of technology and the evaluation of acceptable risk versus cost. A way of evaluating the whole life cost would be to compare current expenditures against those that would be incurred if the best available technology were employed. This only captures avoidance costs and does not consider any of the wider social costs that might be incurred. Business support activities have a small environmental impact through the water distribution system itself. Of greater interest is the impact of carrying out these activities. They all use offices and office facilities, this gives rise to emissions from the office, the generation of waste materials and a range of other impacts. The effects are incremental but if no distribution network existed there would be no requirement for an organisation to run it and therefore such impacts would be avoided.

3.3   Bursts and Leakage

Bursts and leakage in a distribution system increase the volume of water required to deliver the service to the consumer. Therefore a greater demand is placed on resource. The effects are felt throughout the system and therefore it is necessary to trace the consequences of an activity through the system in order to determine the full extent of the impact on environmental characteristics.

3.3.1   Water Supply

Bursts and leakage have the direct effect of requiring more, non-productive, water to be supplied into the system. More resources and inputs are required, such as energy, chemicals and managerial effort, which cost money, for the same or lower level of output and reliability. Thus value is not being added to but taken away from the product and the costs are passed onto the consumer, who is being asked to pay for the operator's inefficiency. More raw water abstraction means that raw water treatment capacity is used unproductively and there is an increase in the associated health and environmental risks that accompany such operations. The operator bears and accounts for these costs. They are seldom identified as environmental costs as they are considered part of the normal operation and maintenance of the system. There are the lost opportunity costs (to society) for not having available for other purposes the treatment capacity, the power used for treatment, the use of chemical and personnel resources.

In addition to these there is the incremental impact on resources. The most direct impacts are those on the physical and ecological characteristics; increased levels of abstraction will impact on hydrological functions and decrease assimilative capacity. Additional pumping leads to more emissions, atmospheric pollution and global warming with consequences for the resistance and resilience of the ecosystem. At the same time there may be impacts restricting the amenity uses and hence values. It is the incremental change in costs with incremental change in impact that is of importance on this case.

3.3.2   Water Distribution

In the short term leakage or bursts may have a direct impact on ecological characteristics, depending on their location. The effects would be short-lived and mostly associated with physical changes, habitat loss or impact on special sites in the landscape. There maybe some localised flooding. On the whole there would not be long term changes to ecological characteristics resulting from bursts. In the case of leakage there may be localised changes resulting from increase availability of water but these would disappear once leakage was addressed. An issue, which is of current concern, is that of the amount of spoil material generated when repairs are effected. Ways in which the amount of spoil can be reduced and the manner in which it is disposed of are receiving attention because of the effects of such measures as landfill tax.

There are issues with respect to the wasteful use of a distribution system's capacity and the associated costs. There is also the question as to what effect the greater utilisation of the system has on the maintenance and repair operations. Intuitively it should have an effect but it may be impossible to detect such changes let alone quantify them. Damage to property, businesses and land use from bursts needs to be included. Generally, the impacts of bursts and leakage on the various environmental characteristics are few, localised and short-lived.

3.3.3   Business Activities

The majority of the business activities associated with bursts and leakage concern the impact on welfare, more specifically the perceptions of the various sectors of the public concerning the quality, reliability, efficiency and safety of the service being provided. Generally the greater the number of bursts or the higher the levels of leakage the poorer will be the perceptions of the public. The operator has to devote more resources, time and effort to reassuring the public, answering questions and other means of improving image. It may also have an effect that trickles through to the market place. Though currently limited to the confidence of shareholders and potential investors, in the future with the introduction of greater competition this may take on an even greater role. More efforts may be devoted to maintaining brand image and market share, all of which have cost as well as other implications.

The excess use of resources will contribute, at the margin, to the work effort required of an organisation and thus a loss of capacity to deal with other issues – again an opportunity cost. There are moves through proposed legislation to internalise some of the societal costs that can arise such as congestion caused by working being carried out to repair bursts or locate and rectify leakage. The plans offer a system of penalties but may not reflect the social costs that arise from increased journey times, increased car emissions and other delays. In addition to this there are the impacts that are generated through raised levels of pollution to air and potentially to land and water from bursts or leakage even though these are of an incremental nature.

3.4   Rehabilitation

Rehabilitation includes the replacement of parts of the water distribution network, the relining of existing pipes or other physical means of upgrading that extend or enhance the operational usefulness of the infrastructure. This generally has a positive effect on levels of leakage and on the frequency and probability of pipe bursts. Rehabilitation has a positive impact on most environmental characteristics, mirroring the negative aspects of bursts and leakages.

3.4.1 Water Supply

Rehabilitation should lead to a reduction in leaks and bursts placing less demand on water resources and reducing impacts on the physical and ecological environmental characteristics that rely on the availability of water. At the same time the improved condition of the pipes should reduce the energy requirements for pumping both through the decrease in volume of water and reduced frictional components, and minimise maintenance needs such as flushing and additional chemical dosing.

The reduced volume required has a beneficial impact in that it extends the availability of the existing supplies and capacity of the infrastructure to meet future demands. This can defer the need for investment in extending parts of the water supply and distribution network. Improvements in performance throughout the network will result in the need for less input resources such as energy, chemicals, labour and other services. Such programmes can improve the general perception of the organisation and have a positive impact on social welfare. The environmental pollution to air, land and water through abstraction, pumping and water treatment can be reduced, which also has a positive impact.

3.4.2 Water Distribution

Improvement of the distribution system should result in lower leakage levels and reduced burst frequency and probability. This being the case there will be a lessening of the need for maintenance and waste detection activities and its associated infrastructure. Work carried out on the network can have both a positive and negative impact on welfare. In the short term the disruption caused by the work leads to congestion, increased journey times and a degree of inconvenience to consumers. In the longer term the perception that the system is more robust and reliable as a result of the work should increase confidence and improve public welfare.

3.4.3   Business Activities

There should be a lessening of the contribution of plant and vehicles to atmospheric pollution and global warming coupled with a reduction of traffic flow problems through a reduction in the number of vehicle trips required to run the system and operate the network. It is likely that a better record on leakage and bursts will promote the perception that the operator is delivering a better, more reliable service and is more eco-efficient in its operations. This impacts not only on the public relations service but also on technical support through the call centres, and customer services. The lessening of this workload should enable efforts to be directed to other areas that require attention and thus it creates opportunities for further improving the service and its reliability. The difficulty would be to be able to provide estimates of the value of this both to the company and to other stakeholders as well. These will be a mix of private benefits to the company as well as benefits to society.

There are positive impacts on the infrastructure side of the organisation in the creation of capacity to pursue other objectives that would add value for the operator. A decrease in leakage and bursts as well as better reliability of the system means that there could be a reduction of the materials holding required, leading to reduced impacts from materials storage, though in reality this may be minimal.

3.5   Social and Environmental Costs

Some work has been carried out on the cost to the environment of abstraction (DETR, 2000). It should be possible in future to relate levels of abstraction with cost and thus associate changes due to bursts, leakage and upgrading with changes in cost. This would indicate costs difference resulting from environmental change.

Emissions to air originate from vehicles and other energy uses such as electricity. The cost to the environment of emissions from vehicles is now partly captured through measures introduced by government. However, actual charges may not reflect the level of environmental damage caused by emissions and this may require further consideration. It should be possible to indicate the environment related proportion of these costs and could be used to indicate the changes in environmental costs of any operational changes. The difficulty of course is to be able to calculate the effect of operational changes, such as bursts, on vehicle use.

The use of electrical energy for pumping or other purposes places a demand on the power generation infrastructure and gives rise to emissions. Because of the remote nature of this relationship the type of fuel used in generation, levels and types of emissions cannot be directly determined. The power generation industry has over recent years been subject to greater controls in order to limit its impact on the environment. It could be argued then that the environmental cost of energy use emissions has to a large extent been internalised and passed on to the customer through the price mechanism. What proportion of the price reflects the cost of environmental regulation (as distinct from environmental cost) will vary for each energy source.

Other emissions originate from treatment works, offices and other fixed site facilities such as workshops. The mix includes thermal emissions, chemicals and dusts, methane generated and others. It should be possible to determine what the emissions are from reference work done in support of the implementation of ISO 14000 or EMAS at the various sites. There is no straightforward way of accounting for the environmental impacts of these emissions and so will require further investigation. The absence of environmental levies or taxes indicates that the costs they impose are not being internalised and so they have to be treated as external costs. Discharges to water are subject to regulation, though this is more evident on the wastewater regulation side of an operator's activity. Discharges are subject to statutory limits the meeting of which imposes costs on the operator that could be identified and accounted for as social and environmental costs.

The image of and confidence that there is in an operator is in part due to the efforts made to maintain and enhance that image and build confidence. It is for this reason that there are public relations activities, customer call centres, time devoted by personnel at all levels to related activities, support to various interest groups, consultation processes, interaction with various government agencies and the regulator. These are tied in with the impact on the socio-economic environment and there are associated costs. For example it may not be possible to determine the cost of management's time devoted to social and environmentally related activities without extensive investigation and analysis. Poor perception of operations or activities by stakeholders can and does give rise to an increase in public relations efforts. Image has an impact on those that regulate the industry as well as those that invest in it and so operators do have a vested interest in managing and being responsive to the views and opinions of stakeholder groups.

Waste generation and management has attracted the attention of European Union and government agencies, arising out of a concern for the environmental and social effects of waste generation and the responsible use of scarce natural resources. Dealing with waste material imposes additional costs that had not previously been made. These costs should be identified as environmental costs for accounting purposes.

3.5.1 Valuation Methodologies

Although it is possible to identify how and where externalities might occur it is less easy to estimate the costs themselves. In some cases the costs of an externality have been internalised through mechanisms, such as taxes, used to simulate market mechanisms and thus create value. The problem remains, however, that in the absence of clear and enforceable property rights and the existence of markets for social and environmental goods and services the task of determining appropriate values remains problematic. Economists have been aware of this problem and over the last two decades a number of approaches to overcome this problem have been developed and applied (Hanley et al., 1997). The range of methodologies available that have been used as a means to determine value include;

- *avoidance costs,* the cost of avoiding damage by say returning the same volume and quality of water to the point of abstraction as was taken out.

- *remediation costs*, the cost of restoring the environment to its original state.

- *willingness-to-pay*, the amount the "public" would be willing to pay to ensure that the environment remains in the same state as it is.

- *willingness-to-accept*, the amount the public would be willing to accept in compensation for allowing a resource to be used and the consequent loss of environmental stock and services.

It is the value of the relative change of impact with change of scale of operation that is of interest rather than a fixed or single environmental cost. This makes the task of valuation even more difficult. The values that are of interest are either the cost of a service provided by the environment or the cost arising from a change in the quality of an environmental resource. Table 3.1 below indicates the various methods available for estimating value.

	OBSERVED BEHAVIOUR	HYPOTHETICAL BEHAVIOUR
DIRECT ESTIMATION	*Direct Observed* Competitive market price Simulated markets	*Direct Hypothetical* Bidding games Willingness-to-pay questions
INDIRECT ESTIMATION	*Indirect Observed* Travel cost Hedonic pricing Avoidance expenditures Referendum voting	*Indirect Hypothetical* Contingent Valuation Methods

Table 3.1 Adapted from Mitchell and Carson (1989), p75

Direct use values can be directly observed in the market place and thus are easier to determine. Direct use values are of interest here when there are changes in quantity or quality that need to be reflected in prices and costs. Indirect use values (functional values), e.g. a service provided by the environment such as flood control, can be investigated via indirect observed behaviour and equating the service with an equivalent technological solution.

Other external costs are a form of non-use value and as such their value has to be inferred indirectly through simulating pseudo-market conditions.

Methods that use indirect observation, as indicated in Table 3.1, include avoidance, defensive or remediation expenditures. The avoidance approach is based on the idea that additional infrastructure can be provided that will not only allow the use of a resource but will then capture it after use and return it to its origin in its original state. By doing so the consequences of use are avoided, but at a cost. Although most of the capital and operating costs can be calculated from market related prices it is also necessary to take into account other associated costs such as the environmental and social costs of providing the additional infrastructure. The attraction of the approach is that it relies on a technical fix for which the costs can be determined with a good degree of accuracy and certainty. The pitfalls are that the costing may not be comprehensive and omit important items. It is often a theoretical approach because there would be no intention of actually investing in such a solution.

Defensive expenditure accepts the current status and assumes that the effects are mitigated by adopting technological fixes. For example, the purchase of air filters to remove air pollutants within an office environment or protective clothing in an aggressive environment would be defensive expenditures. In other words, technological solutions used as a defence against the adverse effects of a degraded environment. The costing of this approach is relatively straightforward in those cases where the technological fixes are available and effective. The major drawback is that it fails to recognise the impacts and cost implications to the wider environment, treating them as being of little or no significance. It therefore seriously underestimates the costs involved.

Remediation is a clean up cost. It has the presumption that it is possible to restore an environment to its pre-use state. The approach can be used where there is a finite timescale to use and there is a presumption of no permanent loss or irreversible change, presumptions that may not be correct. The approach is not well suited to social, welfare, community or economic environments nor are the costs involved for these areas well understood. Its application in those instances where operations are ongoing over a protracted period of time is not recommended. It is good at dealing with physical effects but not much else.

Alternatives to these approaches try to estimate values for environmental characteristics based on simulating a hypothetical market for those environmental goods, a technique known as the Contingent Value Method (CVM). These estimate either the willingness-to-pay or the willingness-to-accept a change in the quality or quantity of an environmental good or service. These bids are used as data from which inference on the shadow price of some environmental gain or loss is drawn. As has been noted, *"in developed countries it has been employed to value water quality improvements, the benefits of reduced air pollution, and the option or existence values of ...ecologically important species"*. (Perman, Ma and McGilvray, 1996). It relies on sample evidence from questionnaires, surveys or simulation analysis to make inferences about a relevant population and it depends on the skill with which the questionnaires or surveys are drawn up and conducted as well as the attitude and characteristics of the respondents.

The problems and applicability of CVM have been extensively reviewed over the years, most notably by a panel of experts appointed by NOAA (National Oceanographic and Atmospheric Administration) as a result of the Exxon Valdez disaster in Alaska. The panel noted that contingent valuation methods *"provide useful, if possibly imperfect, information about values"* (Bishop et al., 1995). CVM is attractive as not only does it potentially have wide applicability to valuation of resource use but it is the only known approach for capturing non-use values associated with environmental assets (Bishop et al., 1995).

To carry out a CVM study requires a significant investment in time and resources. This fact along with general unfamiliarity with the method goes some way to explaining its limited take up. A growing number of CVM studies have however been carried out in the UK. An alternative approach is to make use of the results of other CVM studies using a benefits transfer approach. This adjusts the values found from other studies by taking into account the characteristics of the study area. As an approach it is suitable for desktop studies and to indicate the range of possible values. The Foundation for Water Research has produced *Assessing the Benefits of Surface Water Quality Improvements Manual* (Foundation for Water Research, 1996), which is an example of this approach.

With respect to attempting to value the social cost of, say, changes of employment, a different approach would have to be adopted. The effects manifest themselves throughout the social and economic fabric of society but there may not be clear causal links. Clearly, loss of employment has a direct effect on loss of spending power and a loss of revenue to the state. These can be calculated but it is more difficult to assess other costs that might arise through indirect or secondary effects. These have generally been investigated and calculated on a macro level in the economy. How applicable or transferable this would be to small levels of change of limited geographical extent is an open question and it may be preferable to not include these.

Accounting for internal costs relies on existing information gathered from an operator's transactions. It is mostly a case of gathering that information and representing it in a format that reflects the full cost of an activity. An underlying assumption is that this reflects the full cost of goods and services provided. The cost of externalities cannot be valued and accounted for in the same way and alternative methodologies have to be employed to uncover their value. The available environmental valuation methodologies while not exact are capable of providing useful information about the value of externalities. This can be incorporated into the accounting framework in order to provide a whole life costing for the operation of water distribution networks.

CHAPTER FOUR
Whole Life Cost Accounting Framework *Theory*

4.1   Introduction

This chapter considers how the activities and cost items identified in Chapter 2 can be characterised and built up for their inclusion into the Methodology. A true ABC system that the Methodology is built around, attempts to determine all the cost drivers of providing a service, identifying how they affect costs, and so incorporate them into the accounting system. The drivers determine how costs should be apportioned to a particular part of the network.   However, it may not be practical or possible to determine all the cost drivers. An alternative might be to treat some costs as fixed annual costs and apportion them accordingly. In other words what is proposed is not a true ABC approach but rather a pragmatic approach that seeks to come as close to ABC as can be achieved with the knowledge and information available.

The main focus of this chapter is on operational costs, with the practical implications and limitations in assigning each cost discussed based on an accounting system set up in a similar manner to that described in RAG 4.01.   Although water distribution networks are the main focus of the Methodology, the derivation of the at-boundary on-costs that arise from raw water supply and treatment are discussed.   The costs of supply, bursts and leakage are dealt with in some detail with equations derived that describe how the cost of an item can be linked to a cost driver and unit costs.

The quantification of social (and environmental) costs is much more complex and will not display as simple relationships, like the private costs.   Indeed, it may not be possible at this stage to quantify many of them other than in a rudimentary fashion. Therefore, only passing reference is made to them, with reference made to the discussions within Chapter 3.

4.2   Whole Life Cost

The Whole Life Cost of operating and maintaining a water distribution network is the sum of all the costs of the activities required for operation and maintenance that take place over the period of analysis considered.   Formally this can be represented as follows;

$$WLC = \int_0^T e^{-rt} \left(\mathbf{a}(t) + \mathbf{b}(t) + ... \mathbf{x}(t) + \mathbf{y}(t) + \mathbf{z}(t) \right) dt \qquad (4.1)$$

where, *WLC* is the whole life cost, *T* is the period of analysis, **a, b**,…,**x, y, z** are all the activities undertaken, *r* is the discount rate. The cost of activity **a** at time *t*, **a**(*t*), is given as

$$\mathbf{a}(t) = \mathbf{a}(t)_p + \mathbf{a}(t)_e \qquad\qquad (4.2)$$

where, $\mathbf{a}(t)_p$ is the private cost and $\mathbf{a}(t)_e$ is the external cost of activity **a** at time *t*, and,

$$\mathbf{a} = a(\mathrm{m,n}) \qquad\qquad (4.3)$$

where m is a vector describing the cost function and n a vector describing physical properties that drive the cost function.

Equations 4.1 to 4.3 provide the framework for the Methodology. Implicit in this is a need to understand how the performance of the system changes in response to changes of physical parameters (e.g. age, rehabilitation or changes in operation) that determine and govern its behaviour.

If the framework is to be developed into a management tool then it has to have practical application. The question then arises as to what is the appropriate level of an organisation's activities to apply it. This question is explored in the following section.

4.3   Water Supply: Resources and Treatment Costs

4.3.1   General

This section covers abstraction, raw water transfer and treatment costs. The purpose is to indicate how such costs could be built up and included as an at-boundary on-cost to the WSZ. There is no attempt to link these costs to the performance of the assets at this time, though it is acknowledged that this would be a logical development.

4.3.2   Abstraction

Abstraction covers the procurement of water from either groundwater or surface water sources (rivers and reservoirs). The purchase of water from other sources is also included. The cost will be made up from labour, materials and equipment; and services, as direct and indirect variable and fixed costs. Direct costs would include an allocation of supervision and management costs along with any "fixed" costs. Any "fixed" costs could be apportioned by volume of water supplied or by number of abstraction points. The operator would have to decide the most appropriate method, given the circumstances. The indirect costs could be derived from the business activities; cost of regulation, scientific services and general and support costs but excluding customer services, but this requires a rigorous analysis of time and resources allocated. These costs tend to be gathered and accounted for at a business unit level and not disaggregated at the WSZ level.

Although it would be desirable for all costs to be variable, in practice this may not be possible. For some components the cost remains fixed over a range of abstraction volumes. For example, only when abstraction volume reaches a change point are more resources required to maintain a given level of service and thus costs increase. This results in a stepped cost function. Under most conditions it is unlikely that abstraction will change to such a degree that it would be necessary to derive the step function for fixed costs.

There is an implicit assumption of maximal efficiency, in other words abstraction operations are being carried out in the most efficient manner with the most efficient use of resources. This assumption may or may not be correct and it would be up to the individual operator to decide whether to build in the effect of future efficiency savings on cost.

A cost function will have two components, a fixed cost and a variable cost. The general form of the cost function might therefore be;

$$C_a = \sum A + V_a \sum B \qquad (4.4)$$

where, C_a is the annual private cost of abstraction, A represents the annual fixed costs, V_a is the annual volume of water abstracted and B the variable costs.

In addition to the private costs incurred by the company in abstracting water there are external or public costs associated with abstraction. More details on sources and possible quantification of these social costs are provided in Section 3.2.2.

4.3.3   Raw Water Transfer

Raw water transfer covers the operation and maintenance of the infrastructure that transfers water from the point of abstraction to its point of treatment. It would be preferable if the cost driver were to be the volume of transferred water, as this would allow a degree of consistency within water resources and treatment. These costs though are unlikely to alter, so they would essentially become fixed costs. Fixed costs would display a step function form if there were a need to increase the activities due to some external requirement.

The external costs of water transfer are associated with the support activities rather than the infrastructure itself, under normal operating conditions. As such they would be accounted for and included under those support activity cost headings. Deviations from this would be construction activities. It would be at the discretion of the operator to decide whether this warranted the inclusion of a small amount to cover such eventualities.

4.3.4   Water Treatment

Water treatment covers the running of the processes and infrastructure required to render raw water fit for consumption. In addition to the water there are other raw material inputs, such as chemicals, the potential impacts of which have to be considered. As an industrial process, water treatment produces not just emissions but waste as well that has to be disposed of. The costs of these whether they are borne directly or are external have to be accounted for and included in any cost allocation.

The public costs of water treatment are restricted to those associated with particulate and gaseous emissions as well as the disposal of waste material such as sludge. Sludge waste could go to landfill and therefore the cost of its disposal, which would include landfill tax, would be accounted for. Under most circumstances, sludge would have minor public impacts, as would emission of gaseous and particulate materials. There are risks attached to the running of water treatment works as by their nature they use toxic chemicals. The risks associated with a works will be related to how it is designed, operated and managed. The decision as to whether to include risk related costs is at the discretion of the operator.

4.3.5   Supervision and Management

Rather than try to apportion the supervision and management costs across the abstraction, raw water transfer and treatment, it is suggested that these costs are lumped together as a fixed annual at-boundary input cost for the distribution network. Associated social and environmental costs would relate to the use of vehicles and equipment that have an impact on the external environment.

4.3.6   Input Value of Raw Water Supplied

The input value of raw water supplied is the summation of fixed and variable costs of the abstraction, raw water transfer and treatment plus the indirect cost of supervision and management. As such it is an at-boundary input cost.

4.4   Water Supply: Treated Water Distribution Costs

The treated water distribution costs refer to those incurred in the transfer of the water from the treatment plant through the network and the storage reservoir to the geographical boundary identified for the Methodology.

4.4.1   Treated Water Transfer

Treated water transfer covers the operation of the infrastructure that transfers water from the treatment location to bulk clean water storage before distribution. It is anticipated that most of the costs would be associated with high lift pumping of treated water. In addition there would be the costs associated with the administration, supervision and management of water distribution. Only a portion of these fixed costs would accrue to treated water transfer. Some costs, other than those directly associated with pumping might not vary directly with the volume of water, such as routine maintenance of a pumping installation, related to running hours or routine inspections. Under such circumstances, it may be possible to relate them, indirectly, to volume or to an alternative cost driver such as number of installations of a particular type. Care needs to be exercised as to how the costs are to be characterised and associated with cost drivers.

The social costs of water transfer would be associated with the activities of the support actions – administration, supervision and management rather than with the infrastructure itself, under normal operating conditions such as the impact of vehicle emissions used by maintenance teams. As such they would be accounted for and included under those cost headings.

4.4.2   Treated Water Storage

This includes all treated water service reservoirs and towers, usually treated as the same within the water supply system, secondary disinfection plant on reservoir sites and break pressure tanks. The direct costs would include those associated with the operation and maintenance of service reservoirs and associated installations. Added to this are a proportion of the administration, supervision and management costs associated with water distribution. These costs have to be apportioned across all the different activities that are required to operate and maintain the water distribution system. One scheme for proportioning the costs might be on a time spent basis though it is unlikely that such information would be readily available and it might be simpler to treat these costs as fixed annual costs.

The public costs directly associated with storage are limited as they are fixed installations, the main impact of which might be visual aesthetics. The presence of disinfection equipment and supplies poses a problem if accidents were to occur but under normal operation there should be no impact unless it is shown that some risk, to health for example, exists. The societal impact would be associated with the indirect activities; management, supervision and administration, and as such should be included with them in their cost make up.

4.4.3   Input Value of Treated Water

The input value of treated water is derived by aggregating the calculated cost of both treated water transfer and storage. Within the Whole Life Costing framework this cost is included as an at-boundary input cost in the same way that the costs of raw water supplied are input. This allows the impact of capital maintenance and operational decisions in the distribution network on whole life costs to be accounted for and evaluated, recognising that such decisions can have an influence on the demand for resources from outside of the WSZ considered.

If required, the at-boundary input costs can be determined externally to the Methodology, but still used within the method.

4.5   Distribution

Distribution covers the supply of treated water from service reservoirs into a distribution network that supplies consumers; industrial, commercial, business, public or domestic. Included in the volume of water distributed are leakage, bursts, illegal supplies and unaccounted for water. In order to perform and maintain the supply function a number of activities have to be undertaken, which incur costs. The costs include the day-to-day costs associated with operation and management, routine repair and maintenance, and associated business activity support costs. They also include rehabilitation activities required to meet and maintain performance (referred to as base level) or meet additional (enhanced level) requirements arising from whatever source. Such expenditures[1] will have consequences that affect future performance and costs, for example a programme of mains replacement will lower future leakage and burst costs, lower pumping costs and reduce abstraction charges. The Methodology allows consideration of such actions with the accounting module providing a basis on which to evaluate the costs for their inclusion into the management decision module.

The level of service to customers can be maintained by either the outcome of a planned or unplanned decisions and actions. Unplanned maintenance is a reaction to unforeseen circumstances that require a swift response, such as a pipe burst or a water quality problem – it is reactive rather than proactive. Planned maintenance covers work to be carried out on the distribution system for which provision has been made in terms of either programme or budget. It can encompass such activities as preventative, routine maintenance and capital maintenance (repair, renovation or

---

[1] Expenditures are usually referred to as operational expenditures and capital expenditures to distinguish between day-to-day expenses and others that are seen as related to the provision of infrastructure. The adoption of an extended timescale renders this distinction unnecessary. Within WLC all expenditures are treated as operational as they are required to maintain the system in operation in the long term. In financial accounting terms the difference is necessary and has tax and other implications. It also has implications in terms of how the money is raised and paid for, i.e. the interest payments. These however can be included in the proposed accounting framework.

replacement: collectively referred to as rehabilitation) of parts or all of a system. The distinction between them is often one of scale of the work undertaken rather than substance, but they are usually dealt with in different ways. Capital maintenance is part of the capital budget whilst other, smaller scale works form part of the operational budget. When considering so called "normal" operation this is taken to include the smaller scale maintenance activities that would be routinely included in a planned schedule of work. Normal operation covers the routine, every day activities that are required to ensure that a system is able to operate, such as switching on pumps, reading meters, inspections and so forth.

The costs associated with the distribution system are broken down into three elements: normal supply, bursts and leakage.

4.5.1   Normal Supply

The cost of normal supply is taken to be all the costs incurred in operating a water distribution network (including "at-boundary" costs) to supply water to consumers excluding those costs associated with bursts and leakage (see Figure 2.2). The cost of supply is made up of fixed and variable costs. The volume of water supplied will not be the cost driver in every instance, rather quantities such as length of mains, number of service points (such as valves and chambers), number of personnel and a range of other factors related to the particular activity concerned.

The total cost of normal supply in a distribution network can be represented by Equation 4.5. The costs are specific to the WSZ under consideration, in other words they are geographically specific. Other WSZs can and will have different cost profiles, depending on the characteristics of that zone.

$$C_{supply} = (C_{inputw}+C_{op\&m}+C_{vop\&m}+C_{r\&m}+C_{rrm}+C_{cm}+C_{binspec}+C_{distr}+C_{e\&c}+C_{asm}+C_{wq}+C_{capm})$$

$$+ (C_{reg}+C_{ss}+C_{g\&s}+C_{cs}) \tag{4.5}$$

where, C_{supply} is the annual cost of normal supply for a given WSZ, which is made up of:

C_{inputw} is the annual cost of the input water into the WSZ,

$C_{op\&m}$ is the normal operation and maintenance cost,

$C_{vop\&m}$ is the valve operation and maintenance cost,

$C_{r\&m}$ is the cost of repair and maintenance of service pipes,

C_{rrm} is the cost of replacement and repair of meters (other than consumer meters),

C_{cm} is the cost of installation and replacement of consumer meters,

$C_{binspec}$ is the cost of bye-law inspections,

C_{distr} is the cost of operation and control of the distribution network,

$C_{e\&c}$ is the cost of enquiries and complaints not associated with bursts or leakage,

C_{asm} is the portion of administration, supervision and management costs associated with the distribution system,

C_{wq} is the cost associated with maintaining water quality,

C_{capm} is the cost of capital maintenance works carried out on the system.

And the costs associated with business activities,

C_{reg} is the cost of regulation associated with the WSZ,

C_{ss} is the cost of scientific services associated with the WSZ,

$C_{g\&s}$ is the cost of general and support services associated with the WSZ,

C_{cs} is the cost of customer services associated with the WSZ.

Each of these elements has a private social cost component. The determination of the private costs to be included depends on a number of factors, each of which varies with the type of cost and what drives it. The elements will be discussed in turn, with the likely cost drivers identified.

4.5.1.1   *Input Water*

The cost of the input water, whether derived in line with Sections 4.3 and 4.4 or not, is given by;

$$C_{inputw} = c_f + c_v \cdot v + E_{inputw} \qquad (4.6)$$

where, c_f is the fixed cost of the input water (£/a), c_v is the variable cost of the input water (£/Ml), v is the volume of input water (Ml) and E_{inputw} is the external cost associated with the input water (£/a).

4.5.1.2   *Mains Operation and Maintenance*

The annual cost of normal or planned operation and maintenance of mains in a WSZ is;

$$C_{op\&m} = f_{op\&m} + \sum_i c_{op\&m(i)} \cdot L_{op\&m(i)} + E_{op\&m}) \qquad (4.7)$$

where, $f_{op\&m}$ is the fixed cost of normal operation and maintenance of mains (£/a), i is a set of all combinations of pipe material and diameter in the WSZ, $c_{op\&m(i)}$ is the annual cost per unit length of main (£/m), $L_{op\&m(i)}$ is the length of each main group and $E_{op\&m}$ is the external cost associated with the operation and repair of mains (£/a).

4.5.1.3   *Valves Operation and Maintenance*

The annual cost of operating and maintaining valves and other fixtures and appliances in the network zone is;

$$C_{vop\&m} = f_{vop\&m} + (\sum_j \eta_{vop\&m(j)} N_{vop\&m(j)} c_{vop\&m(j)}) + E_{vop\&m} \qquad (4.8)$$

where, $f_{vop\&m}$ is the fixed cost associated with the operating and maintaining of valves etc., j is a set of all combinations of valve type and diameter in the WSZ, $\eta_{vop\&m}$ is the percentage of each diameter valve group on which work is to be carried out, $N_{vop\&m}$ is the number of valves of a given group j, $c_{vop\&m(j)}$ is the annual operation and maintenance cost of valves of a given valve group and $E_{vop\&m}$ is the social costs associated with the operation and maintenance of valves.

4.5.1.4   *Service Pipe Maintenance and Repair*

The annual cost of repair and maintenance of service pipes is given by;

$$C_{r\&m} = f_{r\&m} + \sum \eta_{r\&m} N_{r\&m} c_{r\&m} + E_{r\&m} \qquad (4.9)$$

where, $f_{r\&m}$ is the fixed cost associated with the repair and maintenance of service pipes (£/a), $\eta_{r\&m}$ is the percentage of service pipes for repair and maintenance, $N_{r\&m}$ is the number of service pipes, $c_{r\&m}$ is the annual repair and maintenance cost (£/unit) and $E_{r\&m}$ is the associated social cost (£/a).

4.5.1.5   District and Zonal Meters

The annual cost of the repair and replacement of district and zonal meters is given by;

$$C_{rrm} = f_{rrm} + \sum_k \eta_{replace(k)} N_{replace(k)} c_{replace(k)} + \sum_k \eta_{repair(k)} N_{repair(k)} c_{repair(k)} + E_{rrm}$$

$$(4.10)$$

where, f_{rrm} is the fixed cost associated with the repair and replacement of the meters (£/a), k is a set of all district and zonal meters in a WSZ, $\eta_{replace}$ and η_{repair} are the percentages of meters of description k to be replaced and repaired, $N_{replace}$ and N_{repair} are the numbers of meters in the WSZ of description k to be replaced and repaired, $c_{replace}$ and c_{repair} are the respective costs for the replacement and repair of meters of description k (£/unit) and E_{rrm} is the social cost associated with the repair and replacement of meters (£/a).

4.5.1.6   Consumer Meter Repairs

The annual cost of the repair and replacement of consumer meters is given by;

$$C_{cm} = f_{cm} + \sum \eta_{cmreplace(l)} N_{cmreplace(l)} c_{cmreplace(l)} + \sum \eta_{cmrepair(l)} N_{cmrepair(l)} c_{cmrepair(l)} + E_{cm}$$

$$(4.11)$$

where, f_{cm} is the fixed cost associated with the repair and replacement of consumer meters (£/a), l is a set of all consumer meter diameters in the WSZ, $\eta_{cmreplace}$ and $\eta_{cmrepair}$ are the percentages of consumer meters to be repaired or replaced respectively, $N_{cmreplace}$ and $N_{cmrepair}$ are the numbers of consumer meters of description l to be replaced or repaired, $c_{cmreplace}$ and $c_{cmrepair}$ are the respective costs for the replacement or repair of consumer meters of description l (£/unit) and E_{cm} is the social cost associated with the repair and replacement of consumer meters (£/a).

4.5.1.7   Byelaw Inspections

The annual cost of byelaw inspections is given by;

$$C_{binspec} = N_{binspec} c_{binspec} + E_{binspec} \qquad (4.12)$$

where, $N_{binspec}$ is the number of inspections, $c_{binspec}$ is the unit cost of inspection (£/inspection), $E_{binspec}$ is the associated social cost (£/a).

4.5.1.8   Distribution Operation and Control

The annual cost of operation and control of distribution is given by;

$$C_{distr} = \alpha \cdot (f_{distr} + E_{distr}) \qquad (4.13)$$

where, α is a factor determined by the operator representing the proportion of the costs of operation and control of distribution to be allocated to a WSZ, f_{distr} is the fixed cost of the operation and control of distribution at company level (£/a) and E_{distr} is the social cost associated with the operation and control of distribution (£/a).

4.5.1.9   *Enquiries and Complaints*

With respect to enquiries and complaints it is noted that the fact that an operator provides a service and therefore interacts with the public and customers will give rise to enquiries and complaints. These may be related to requests for information, queries about bills, complaints about service, passing on information (which may require some action to be taken) or to works related matters. The occurrence of an incident, such as a pipe burst, may generate enquiries and/or complaints. Such incidents might be planned, as in the case of relaying water mains, or unplanned as in the case of a pressure burst. Incidents may be internal to the distribution system or external, such as an interruption to a trunk main, though both will affect the public and customers.

Enquiries and complaints can comprise base and variable loads. Base load will depend on factors such as the relationship between the operator, customers and the public, paperwork generated, image, and numerous other factors. In the end it may be said that there is a number of enquiries, complaints etc. that can be assumed. There is a degree of flexibility that can be built into what is considered to constitute the base load. In some instances, it might include all those complaints for which there is no perceived or obvious driver. Variable load depends on the number of complaint inducing incidents and this will be determined by the performance of the network. So, if the performance is predictable then so can be the probable number of incidents. A reasonable prediction is dependent upon having a reasonable performance model.

It is assumed that an incident can give rise to a number of enquiries and that the enquiry/complaint will be about different effects of the incident. Thus a burst may give rise to complaints about low pressure, water quality or no water as well as about the burst itself.

There is a further factor that has not been explicitly included in this formulation and that is the propensity to complain. Firstly, this may vary with geographic location and secondly it may change over time. Analysis of complaint and performance data could determine this.

The number of complaints arising from an incident will be determined by, among other factors, number of customers affected, location, time, type of incident, type of customer. On the other hand as it is the handling of enquiries and complaints that is of interest it might reasonably be assumed that the cost of handling will be uniform and invariant with type of complaint. The number of complaints can be represented by;

$$N_{comp} = n_b + \sum n_{ti} \cdot N_{ti} \qquad (4.14)$$

where, N_{comp} is the total number of complaints etc. received, n_b is the base load complaints etc., ti is a set of incident types, n_{ti} is the number of incidents of a particular type, N_{ti} is the number of complaints generated by a particular type of incident.

The cost of enquiries and complaints is made up of two components and includes the costs associated with receiving and handling complaints/enquiries/queries. Most of the handling cost would be under Business Activities, so care must be taken in the allocation of costs to avoid double accounting. Secondly, there are the costs associated with the reaction to complaints/enquiries/queries.

The cost of handling the complaints depends directly on the number and type of complaints. Most of the costs associated with handling of enquiries and complaints would be accounted for under Business Activities and so care needs to be exercised in the allocation of costs to avoid double accounting. It might be reasonable to assume that the handling cost will be uniform and invariant with the type or nature of the enquiry or complaint and that the cost depends directly on the number of enquiries and complaints. It is felt appropriate to distinguish between the costs of enquiries and complaints related to normal supply and those arising for other reasons.

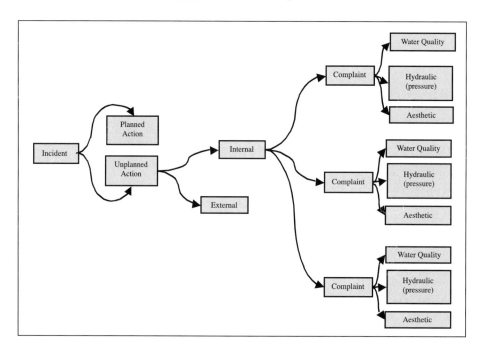

Figure 4.1: Complaints

4.5.1.9.1   Cost of Handling Enquiries and Complaints

The associated cost of handling enquiries and complaints would be;

$$C_{comp} = f_{comp} + c_{comp} \cdot N_{comp} + E_{comp} \qquad (4.15)$$

where, C_{comp} is the total cost of handling enquiries and complaints, f_{comp} is the fixed cost associated with handling enquiries and complaints (£/a), c_{comp} is the unit cost of handling a complaint etc (£/complaint), N_{comp} is the number of complaints received and E_{comp} is the social cost(£/a).

The cost attributable to normal operations, other than bursts and leakage would be;

$$C_{normcomp} = \beta_n \cdot C_{comp} \qquad (4.16)$$

where, β_n is the proportion attributable to normal operations.

4.5.1.9.2   Cost of Investigating Enquiries and Complaints

The total cost of investigating enquiries and complaints is made up from the costs arising from enquiries and complaints related to "normal" operation (i.e. a base load of complaints) and from departures from the norm (which could be bursts, water quality or other-factor related). Though the cause of the departure from the norm may vary, the consequence will be the same: either a burst or leakage or water quality problems or a combination of them. So for normal operation a certain percentage of the total number is assumed and so the cost becomes;

$$C_{icom} = f_{icom} + c_{bi}n_b + \beta_n \sum c_{ti}n_{ti} + E_{icom} \qquad (4.17)$$

where, C_{icom} is the total cost of investigating complaints etc. attributable to normal supply, f_{icom} is the fixed cost associated with the investigation of enquiries and complaints (£/a), c_{bi} is the unit cost of investigating non-incident related enquiries and complaints (£/complaint), n_b is base number of complaints, c_{ti} is the unit cost of investigation and n_{ti} is the number of incidents per type of incident (ti) and E_{icom} is the social cost associated with investigations of enquiries and complaints (£/a).

It is assumed that there will be a difference in the cost of investigating different types of enquiries or complaint. But an incident can give rise in some instances to a number of different types of enquiries or complaints. Investigation of loss of supply, due to a burst for example, may be less expensive to investigate than say discolouration but conversely it may give rise to a complaint about discolouration. This may need to be revisited as more work is carried out.

Therefore the total cost of enquiries and complaints attributable to normal supply of a water distribution network is given by;

$$C_{e\&c} = C_{normcomp} + C_{icom} \qquad (4.18)$$

4.5.1.10   *Administration, Supervision and Management Costs*

The administration, supervision and management activities ensure the proper, efficient and effective running of a distribution network. As an overall function it supports a number of other activities including operation, maintenance, monitoring, investigations and dealing with bursts and leakages amongst others. Its costs, C_{asm} should be proportioned across these different activities, rather than being directly allocated to supply alone.

4.5.1.11   Cost of Capital Maintenance

The cost of capital works maintenance is determined by how much of the distribution network within a water supply zone is to be either replaced or rehabilitated. The costs to be included here must only be the costs that are attributable to the distribution network for reasons other than as a reactive response to bursts or leakage, which are repair activities. In other words, it is a result of a planned series of pre-emptive actions designed to maintain or enhance system performance. The costs will be determined by the characteristics of the pipe groups to be rehabilitated (pipe material and diameter), the location of the work, the replace/rehabilitate methodology chosen and the lengths of mains to be rehabilitated. Included should be the costs associated with contracts or procurement that would come under Business Activities, these are allocated across activities and are included. The cost of additional interest payments and other finance charges should be included in the direct costs.

The cost of capital maintenance is;

$$C_{capm} = f_{capm} + \sum_x l_x \sum_y \Gamma_y \sum_z c_z + E_{capm} \qquad (4.19)$$

where, f_{capm} is a fixed cost item (£/a), l_x is the length of each pipe group x in a WSZ to be rehabilitated, x is a set of pipe groups by material and diameter, Γ_y is a set of locational based (y) cost modifiers, c_z is the unit cost for rehabilitation method z and E_{capm} is the social cost associated with the rehabilitation or replacement work (£/a).

4.5.1.12   Business Activities

To these direct costs now have to be added the indirect costs associated with Business Activities that are applicable to water supply services. Although there are no steadfast rules to determine how the costs of business activities should be allocated to WSZ, suggestions are made as to the basis for allocation. In each case it has to be decided what is the principle cost driver and thus will be used as the basis of allocation. The components of business activity costs are indicated in Equation 4.5.

4.5.1.12.1   Cost of Regulation

The cost of regulation C_{reg} attributed to the distribution of supply could be spread equally between all the DMAs.

$$C_{reg} = (C_{\Sigma reg} / N_{DMA}) + E_{reg} \qquad (4.20)$$

where, N_{DMA} is the number of DMAs being considered, $C_{\Sigma reg}$ is the total cost of regulation for water supply as a whole (£/a) and E_{reg} is the social cost associated with regulation (£/a).

4.5.1.12.2   Customer Service Costs

Customer services can be mostly attributed to supply and could be allocated on the basis of number of customers. However, some of the costs are associated with dealing with enquiries, queries and complaints. It is therefore suggested that a split be made between them to separate out these costs. The costs associated with complaints etc. would be added to the cost of handling of customer complaints and enquiries that is described in Equations 4.16 to 4.18.

$$C_{cs} = (C_{\Sigma cus} \cdot c_{\Sigma cusenq}) / N_{cus} + E_{cs} \qquad (4.21)$$

where, N_{cus} is the number of customers in the area under consideration, $C_{\Sigma cus}$ is the total cost of customer services per customer (£/customer), $c_{\Sigma cusenq}$ is the proportion of the total cost attributable to handling customer enquiries etc., and E_{cs} is the social cost associated with customer services (£/a).

4.5.1.12.3   Scientific Services Costs

Scientific services are mostly applicable to supply distribution.   The costs are associated with the investigation and analysis of particular and potential problems, for example of a water quality nature.   In addition, a certain amount of administrative work is carried out associated with quality reviews as well as supervision and management of the service provided. Some of the costs arise as a result of customer enquiries and complaints. It might, in theory, be possible to determine both a fixed cost and a variable cost, dependent upon the type of investigation and analysis carried out. However, whether it would be cost effective to undertake such an exercise, and whether the results would be sufficiently robust, would have to be determined. An alternative approach would be to assume that the cost driver is related to some physical feature of the distribution system, such as volume of water supplied and to use a scaling factor based on this to determine the cost attributable to a particular water supply zone.   Separated out from this are those costs that arise from the handling of customer enquiries etc. These costs are included with the overall cost of handling customer enquiries that is described in Equation 4.16.

$$C_{ss} = \omega_{ss} (C_{\Sigma ss} - c_{\Sigma ssenq}) + E_{cs} \qquad (4.22)$$

where, ω_{ss} is a scaling factor, $C_{\Sigma ss}$ is the total cost of scientific services attributable to water supply (£/a), $c_{\Sigma ssenq}$ is the total cost associated with handling of enquiries (£/a) and E_{ss} is the social cost associated with scientific services (£/a).

4.5.1.12.4   General and Support Costs

General and support activities apply to all aspects of water supply including activities associated with bursts and leakage. Their allocation is a difficult matter as they cover a wide range of different activities. Ideally the cost of each of the activities would be allocated to a WSZ based on its cost driver.   Whilst such an allocation would represent a truer reflection of the costs incurred, the time and effort require to analyse an operator's expenditures would be significant and unlikely to have greater accuracy and predictive power than simpler approaches. The approach proposed assumes that all of these costs can be allocated to normal water supply operations with the exception of the costs associated with providing, running and maintaining a call centre.

The costs associated with a call centre arise because of enquiries, complaints, queries and a host of other reasons. Some of these will result from incidents such as bursts, leakage, water quality or other departures from the norm.   This cost item is apportioned between normal supply, bursts and leakage. The exact basis, or indeed making such an apportionment at all would have to be determined by the operator.

$$C_{g\&s} = \delta \, (C_{\Sigma g\&s} - c_{\Sigma info}) + E_{g\&s} \qquad\qquad (4.23)$$

where, δ is a non-dimensional scaling factor (e.g. the ratio between total volume of water supplied and that supplied in the zone), $C_{\Sigma g\&s}$ is the total cost of general and support activities attributable to water supply (£/a), $c_{\Sigma info}$ is the total cost of information services associated with call centres for customers (£/a) and $E_{g\&s}$ is the social and environmental cost associated with general and support activities (£/a).

4.5.1.13   *Water Quality*

The costs associated with the handling and investigation of complaints related to water quality follow the same form as that for normal operation. The cost of handling water quality related complaints is given by,

$$\beta_{wq} \cdot C_{comp} \qquad\qquad (4.24)$$

where, β_{wq} is the proportion of the total number of complaints and enquiries related to water quality issues. The cost of investigating a water quality related complaints is,

$$\beta_{wq} \sum_{i=1}^{N} c_{ti} \cdot n_{ti} + E_{icom} \qquad\qquad (4.25)$$

The costs associated with maintaining water quality are made up of several components, as water quality is not a single measure. In respect of a given water quality determinant, within the WLC approach an equation is used to reflect the operational cost of dealing with the risk *(where actions are taken to mitigate the risk)* or financial risk costs carried by the company *(where no action is taken to mitigate the risk)*. A number of prominent water quality determinants have been chosen for consideration. Equations are set out to reflect the cost of flushing to mitigate the risk of discolouration (C_{Tflush}), the risk cost of contravening the poly-aromatic hydrocarbon standard (C_{PAH}), risks associated with disinfection (C_{THM}) and its control of bacteria (C_{BAC}). These are summarised in Equation 4.26 below. Each of the parts of the expression are derived from different sets of equations. Although these equations do not form a performance model *per se*, the cost equations have a physical basis and are dealt with and set out in Chapter 8 as Equations 8.1 to 8.5.

$$C_{wq} = C_{Tflush} + C_{PAH} + C_{THM} + C_{BAC} \qquad\qquad (4.26)$$

4.5.2   Bursts

Mains bursts are structural failures of a pipe or main such that it can no longer perform its proper function or represent a visible failure of the system to the customers. Action is required to restore the functioning of the system, usually through repair of the burst section of main. By its nature this is an unplanned event, that brings with it a number of consequences, each of which have an associated cost. A burst may give rise to a number of enquiries, each incurring costs. These costs will have a social element on top of the private cost to the operator. There is uncertainty about the probable number of bursts occurring in any year. By using an appropriate model it is possible to forecast the probable number of bursts and to allow for the effects of different operational and capital investment decisions on this probable number. The likely or expected total cost associated with bursts for a given year can then be calculated.

The full cost of a burst is made up of several components and not just the direct cost of repair. It includes the value of the water lost, the indirect costs that the operator has to bear as well as external (social and environmental) costs. Indirect costs include the costs of handling complaints and enquiries that arise from a burst, the regulatory compliance costs, compensation payments to those affected, the potential penalty costs imposed by the regulator if performance over a period of time is considered to be unsatisfactory. There are also image costs to be considered. The operator incurs costs in addressing the concerns of its regulators, consumers and the public and in trying to maintain a positive image. It includes the work not just on public relations but also the work time and effort that is needed to address the concerns at the expense of other, more productive activities. These are direct image costs but beyond this there is potential cost of loss of trust. Whilst at the moment operators have geographic monopolies this aspect may be ignored, greater competition in the future may alter this and image costs may increase.

In a wider context there can be other costs such as congestion and disruption and the loss of confidence. Congestion and disruption costs would arise when the public, other than customers, are affected by a burst. This can be captured to a large extent by factoring in the cost impact on traffic delays. As techniques become more advanced and sophisticated it may be possible to extend the range of costs included here such as impact on insurance or on cost of capital. The value of loss of confidence could be captured through the use of willingness-to-pay techniques (for a lower level of bursts). This is a forgone cost that is not available to the operator and is akin to the value placed on "good will" in some businesses. While operators do not compete against each other for custom such costs can be ignored but they may in the future become "real" to the businesses.

The wider social and environmental costs associated with actions should not be forgotten. Although in most cases the environmental impacts and costs associated with the repair of bursts will be minor and of short duration, they should at least be recognised.

There is a danger of double accounting in determining the full range of costs associated with bursts. This could occur in the case of image costs, compensation payments and penalties. As some of these costs are incurred as a result of deviation from the norm their costs should not be included under normal supply. Misallocation will have the effect of overstating the cost of normal operation whilst understating that of bursts. There will also be indirect costs associated with the administration of remedial actions – repair contracts for example, which have the potential to be lost in normal supply. In most cases it would be reasonable to associate the incremental or marginal cost of these activities with bursts and include them on a per burst basis. This approach is not suitable in the case of penalties that might be imposed as a result of an assessment of overall performance. Penalty costs should be linked to performance.

The cost of a burst can be characterised as;

$$C_{burst} = C_{repair} + C_{indB} + C_{extB} \; (+ \; C_{wB}) \tag{4.27}$$

where, C_{burst} is the full cost of a burst, C_{repair} is the cost of repairing a burst, C_{indB} is the indirect cost associated with a burst, C_{extB} is the external cost associated with a burst and C_{wB} is the cost of water lost through a burst.

Although C_{wB} is (nominally) included in many instances it may be easier to ignore this and account for the cost of water lost totally under leakage for practical reasons. It will marginally understate the cost of bursts but given the margin of error on some of the other aspects this is not thought likely to be significant.

4.5.2.1   *Cost of Burst Repair*

The cost of repair will be a function of the number of bursts, pipe diameter, material and depth of cover as well as location of the burst. It should be possible to assign a series of probable costs of repair determined by these characteristics.

$$C_{repair} = \sum_i n_i \sum_j c_j \qquad (4.28)$$

where, n_i is the number of burst events for pipe group i, j is a set of location based costs and c_j is the cost of repair (£).

4.5.2.2   *Indirect Burst Costs*

The indirect costs associated with structural failure, as described above are;

$$C_{indB} = C_{regB} + C_{compen} + C_{compl} + C_{imageB} + C_{penb} \qquad (4.29)$$

where, C_{regB} is the annual regulatory cost associated with structural failures, C_{compen} is the cost of compensation paid to customers and third parties, C_{compl} is the annual operation cost of dealing with complaints and C_{imageB} is the annual image cost associated with structural failures.

4.5.2.3   *Regulatory Bursts Costs*

The annual regulatory costs associated with structural failure may be taken as;

$$C_{regB} = N_{bursts} \cdot c_{regB} + E_{reg} \qquad (4.30)$$

where, N_{bursts} is the total number of structural failures taking place in a water supply zone, c_{regB} is the unit marginal regulatory cost to the operator of a structural failure (£/burst) and E_{reg} is the external cost associated with meeting regulation requirements (£/a).

4.5.2.4   *Burst Compensation Costs*

The annual cost of compensation is derived from that due to customers affected by a structural failure plus compensation paid to third parties. There are guidelines that determine whether customers are entitled to compensation and how much that would be. In the case of compensation to third parties the amount that would be determined by the loss suffered will vary on a case by case basis and be location dependent.

$$C_{comp} = \sum \varepsilon N_{bursts} c_{bcomp} + \sum N_{3P} c_{3Pcomp} \qquad (4.31)$$

where, ε is the proportion of customers affected by a structural failure entitled to compensation, N_{burst} is the number of customers affected by a burst, c_{bcomp} is the customer compensation entitlement (£/customer), N_{3P} is the number of third parties entitled to compensation and c_{3Pcomp} is the compensation entitlement (£/party).

4.5.2.5   *Burst Complaint Costs*

The cost of burst complaints, like that for those associated with normal operation of the water distribution network is made up of the cost of handling the complaints and the cost of investigating the complaints and enquiries received.

$$C_{complaint} = C_{compl} + C_{invburst} \qquad (4.32)$$

4.5.2.5.1   Handling Burst Complaints

The cost of handling complaints is;

$$C_{compl} = \eta \cdot N_{burst} \cdot c_{compl} + E_{compl} \qquad (4.33)$$

where, η is a scaling factor relating number of customers complaining to a structural failure, N_{burst} is the number of structural failures experienced ($N_{ti} = N_{burst}$), c_{compl} is the unit marginal cost of handling complaints and enquiries arising from a structural failure (£/item) and E_{compl} is the social cost associated with handling of complaints (£/a).

4.5.2.5.2   Investigation of Burst Complaints

The cost of investigation of bursts is (refer to Equation 4.17),

$$C_{invburst} = \beta_{burst} \sum_{ti=1}^{N} c_{ti} \cdot n_{ti} + E_{icom} \qquad (4.34)$$

where, β_{burst} is the proportion of the total number of complaints and enquiries related to bursts. Fixed costs are not included in the above equations as it is the marginal costs associated with these incidents that are of interest.

4.5.2.6   *Image Burst Costs*

Image costs are modelled as;

$$C_{imageB} = N_{burst} \cdot c_{imageB} + E_{image} \qquad (4.35)$$

where, N_{burst} is the number of structural failures, c_{imageB} is the unit marginal image cost and E_{image} is the external costs associated with maintaining a positive public image.

4.5.2.7   *Burst Penalty Costs*

The occurrence of a burst event can lead to a reduced service to customers. If there is a regulatory regime in place that sets and monitors standards of service, repeated service failure due to bursts may not be acceptable and the regulator may impose financial penalties. The scale of penalties could be a function of the number, frequency and severity of bursts, depending on the regulatory system and the attitude of the regulator. Records of required levels of service, operator performance and financial penalties imposed would have to be examined in order to decide on whether to include an allowance and if so what an appropriate formulation might be.

$$C_{penb} = f(N_{burst})$$ (4.36)

4.5.2.8   *External Burst Costs*

The external costs have been identified as being related to disruption caused and unrealised willingness-to-pay. There are guidelines issued by UKWIR and it is possible, as suggested by the UKWIR Report (98/RG/01/1), that these can be determined by a Contingent Valuation Method. Disruption costs to traffic flows may be calculated and the reader is referred to that work. In the case of willingness-to-pay, this is usually determined on a case by case basis, though it is possible to use a benefits transfer approach. In view of the nature of these costs and the doubts in some quarters as to whether they should realistically be included, they will not be discussed here.

$$C_{extB} = C_{disrup} + C_{WTP}$$ (4.37)

where, C_{disrup} the total cost of disruption as calculated from the UKWIR manual and C_{WTP} is the total willingness-to-pay for a lower level of bursts.

$$C_{WTP} = = N_{cust} \int_{L1}^{L2} \Delta(WTP)$$ (4.38)

where, N_{cust} is the number of customers in a water supply zone, $\Delta(WTP)$ is the change in willingness-to-pay and $L1$ & $L2$ are different levels of burst frequency.

4.5.3 Leakage

The cost of leakage is determined by the leakage detection strategy adopted, the value of water lost, the indirect and external costs associated with leakage and its control. The costs associated with reacting to leakage through programmes of mains replacement are not included as it is taken as part of the capital maintenance work. An active leakage detection strategy may be more costly initially than a passive strategy but this may decrease substantially over time as the benefits from an associated capital maintenance strategy work their way through the system. It will also depend on the indirect costs such as regulatory costs, image costs, possible penalties and the value of the water lost. The regulation covers the administrative costs arising out of reports to and interaction with the various regulators, at the margin, associated with leakage and dealing with related complaints and enquiries. In addition if leakage levels are at levels that are unacceptable to the regulatory regime there may be the threat of penalties. This is determined by performance over a period of time and not related to individual incidents. Penalties could be associated with leakage volumes and leakage performance. The image cost comprises the additional PR expenditure by an operator required to maintain a positive public image. As there will already exist public relations efforts, only the marginal cost should be included. Marginal costs may vary with level of leakage for the operator's geographic area of operation. It would have to be decided whether it would be worthwhile including this degree of sophistication given the level of information available. External costs include what customers would be willing to pay for a reduction in leakage. The operator forgoes this notional amount by having that level of leakage, and it could be thought of as the value of loss of goodwill, confidence or brand image. It may be possible, as suggested by the UKWIR Report (98/RG/01/1), that these can be determined by a Contingent Valuation Method. In the absence of competition these costs are even more notional than might be the case normally and it is a moot point as to whether they need be included under current circumstances. They would certainly not be of interest to the economic regulator in motivating a case for a certain capital renewal strategy but may be of interest to the operator as additional motivation in choosing between options. Furthermore, care must be taken not to account for them twice, in both leakage and bursts.

$$C_{leak} = C_{lds} + C_{indL} + C_{extL} + C_w \qquad (4.39)$$

where, C_{leak} is the total cost of leakage, C_{lds} is the annual cost for a given leakage detection strategy, C_{indL} is the annual indirect cost of leakage, C_{extL} is the annual external cost of leakage and C_w is the annual cost of water lost.

4.5.3.1   *Leakage Detection Strategy Costs*

The annual cost in undertaking leakage detection can be given as;

$$C_{lds} = f_{lds(a)} + c_{lds(a)} \cdot L + E_{lds(a)} \qquad (4.40)$$

where, $f_{lds(a)}$ is the fixed cost associated with a leakage detection strategy a (£/a), $c_{lds(a)}$ is the variable cost associated with that leakage detection strategy (£/unit) and $E_{lds(a)}$ is the social cost associated with the leakage detection strategy (£/a).

4.5.3.2   *Indirect Leakage Costs*

The indirect costs associated with leakage are;

$$C_{indL} = C_{regL} + C_{complaint} + C_{imageL} \qquad (4.41)$$

where, C_{regL} is the annual regulatory cost associated with leakage, $C_{complaint}$ is the annual operation cost of dealing with complaints and C_{imageL} is the annual image cost associated with leakage.

4.5.3.3   *Leakage Regulatory Costs*

The annual regulatory costs associated with leakage may be taken as;

$$C_{regL} = N_{cust}P_{reg}c_{reg} + E_{reg} \qquad (4.42)$$

where, N_{cust} is the number of customers, P_{reg} is the probability that the customer will complain about leakage or a leak, c_{reg} is the marginal unit cost of regulation requirements (£/complaint) and E_{reg} is the social cost associated with regulation (£/a).

4.5.3.4   *Leakage Complaints Costs*

As with Normal Supply and Burst, the cost of leakage complaints is the sum of the handling and investigation of the enquiries and complaints.

4.5.3.4.1   Handling Leakage Complaints

The cost of handling complaints associated with leakage is;

$$C_{compl} = \rho \cdot N_{cust} \cdot c_{cuscompl} + E_{cuscompl} \qquad (4.43)$$

where, ρ is a scaling factor relating number of customers with the number likely to lodge an enquiry about a leakage related matter, N_{cust} is the number of customers in a water supply zone, $c_{cuscompl}$ is the unit marginal cost of handling complaints and enquiries from customers (£/item) and $E_{cuscompl}$ is the social cost associated with handling of complaints (£/a).

4.5.3.4.2   Investigating Leakage Complaints

The cost of investigation of leakage is (refer to Equation 4.17),

$$C_{invl} = \beta_{leak} \sum_{i=1}^{N} c_{ti} \cdot n_{ti} + E_{icom} \qquad (4.44)$$

where, β_{leak} is the proportion of the total number of complaints and enquiries related to leakage.

In the case of leakage it is difficult to link together the prediction of leakage and leakage target levels with incidents that would give rise to complaints. Complaints in this respect may have more to do with a propensity to complain rather than to do with system performance. An alternative approach that may have merit would be to consider complaints that might be related to leakage as part of either the base load or normal operation and then to consider what factors other than system performance drive complaints and include this.

4.5.3.5   *Leakage Image Costs*

The image cost associated with leakage can be taken as ;

$$C_{imageL} = N_{cust} \cdot c_{imageL} + E_{image} \qquad (4.45)$$

where, N_{cust} is the number of customer failures, c_{imageL} is the unit marginal image cost (£/item) and E_{image} is the social costs associated with maintaining a positive public image (£/a).

4.5.3.6   *Leakage Penalty Costs*

If there is a regulatory regime in place that sets and monitors standards of service, repeated failure to meet leakage targets may not be acceptable and the regulator may impose financial penalties. The scale of penalties could be a function of the leakage volume and target set, depending on the regulatory system and the attitude of the regulator. Records of required levels of service, operator performance and financial penalties imposed would have to be examined in order to decide on whether to include an allowance and if so what an appropriate formulation might be.

$$C_{penl} = f(Leakage\ Level) \qquad (4.46)$$

4.5.3.7   *External Costs*

The external cost, taken as willingness-to-pay and confidence may be represented in simplistic terms;

$$C_{extL} = C_{WTP} \qquad (4.47)$$

and

$$C_{WTP} = N_{cust} \int_{L1}^{L2} \Delta(WTP) \qquad (4.48)$$

where, N_{cust} is the number of customers in a water supply zone, $\Delta(WTP)$ is the change in willingness-to-pay, *L1* & *L2* are different levels of leakage.

4.6   Summary

In deriving an accounting framework an Activity Based Costing approach is proposed to determine the costs of operational activities. Costs are associated with an action or driver making it possible to link unit costs to performance of the network, the cost drivers, over the service life and to determine the whole life cost of operation. Network performance is also a consequence of rehabilitation actions (capital maintenance) and these must be included.

The difficulties of including and accounting for external costs should not be underestimated and a great deal of work and analysis will be required to achieve this. Such costs are both location specific and diffuse in society and the environment. At this stage it may not be possible, practical, or in some cases desirable to include them as actual costs. But their inclusion is recommended and the effect on management options and outcomes should be investigated in order to motivate greater sustainability in the operation of water distribution networks.

CHAPTER FIVE
Whole Life Cost Accounting
Framework *Implementation*

5.1   Introduction

Chapter 5 presents the implementation of a cost accounting framework that can be used in conjunction with distribution network performance models and decision support software. Whereas Chapter 4 provides a theoretical view of the various cost items and activities to be included in a WLC accounting scheme, this chapter provides a practical means to derive values from the cost information that will be observed in most water companies and authorities around the world. It presents the main features of a generic model used to derive unit costs from operational cost data, and compiling it into a format that is compatible with the Decision Tool. Costs within the framework are broken down into three categories: the costs associated with the normal supply of water to customers, the costs associated with bursts, and those with leakage. What is required is an approach that takes all the costs incurred and allocates them to one of the three categories on a rational basis. The rational basis must reflect not just the physical reality of moving water from the point of abstraction to the consumer, but also the way cost information is categorised and stored by the operator.

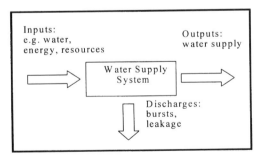

Figure 5.1: Input/Output Diagram for a Water Supply System

As a starting point to meet this objective, consider a water supply system as a simple input/output model as provided in Figure 5.1. A water supply system transforms inputs (e.g. raw water, energy and other resources) into outputs – a water supply service that meets amongst others, the statutory quality requirements. In doing so there is waste in the form of discharges such as bursts and leakage. The resources input are not costless and therefore the outputs have costs associated with and apportioned to them.

The physical configuration of the water supply system will also be an important factor in the costs incurred in supplying the service. Figure 5.2 shows an idealised system where the water is first abstracted from a source. The water is then conveyed to a point where it is treated and rendered potable. From the treatment works it is transferred to a storage facility that feeds water into a distribution network. Each of these stages requires infrastructure, the functioning of which requires activities and inputs (resources).

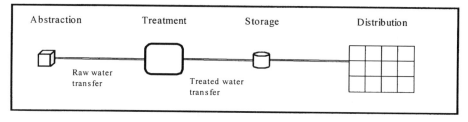

Figure 5.2: Idealised Water Supply System

For each of the stages in Figure 5.2 a description of each of the activities undertaken will be required that allows inputs and resources required for each of these stages. Ofwat's Regulatory Accounting Guidelines 4.01 (Ofwat, 1992), guidelines for the Analysis of Operating Costs and Assets provides a schema for this. As water companies in England and Wales are required to report operating costs according to this, it provides an ideal starting point for categorising and handling operational costs. Figure 5.3 provides an overview of RAG 4.01. Details outlining what is included as part of each of the cost items under the various main headings are provided in RAG 4.01. Though RAG 4.01 is used as the example, the approach is sufficiently flexible that it could be transposed to other situations, as the treatment of operational and capital maintenance costs would be similar.

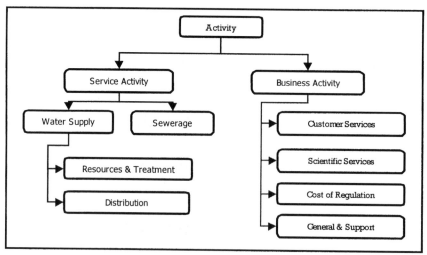

Figure 5.3: Overview of RAG 4.01 Activities

In determining the cost of providing a water supply service, it is not just the direct costs that are required to be considered, but also the business activity costs that support and underpin these direct activities. The various business activity costs; scientific services; customer services; regulation; and general and support activities are allocated to supply, bursts and leakage depending on how they are incurred in support of them. For example, customer services supports the normal supply of water and thus the cost of this activity should be allocated as part of the overall cost of normal supply. On the other hand some of the cost of regulation will be driven by bursts, leakage and normal supply. Therefore, the allocation for the cost of regulation should reflect this.

The costs for the three categories of supply, bursts and leakage can be built up from the basis represented in Figures 5.2 and 5.3, which follow the passage of water from source to customer. Figure 5.4 indicates the way these three categories of cost are built up.

In addition to the operational costs, information on capital maintenance and operational intervention activities is required. The Decision Tool may also require estimates of the expected efficiency gains over time for various activities and interventions. Lastly, the cost model requires information on the scale of penalty costs to reflect the consequences of non-compliance with levels of service set for an operator by regulators.

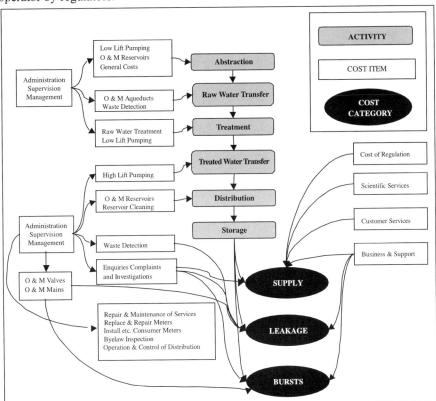

Figure 5.4: Breakdown of Activities and Cost Items in RAG 4.01

Costs within the accounting framework could be split into Labour related costs,[1] Materials and Equipment[2] costs, Service[3] costs and, Social and Environmental (External) costs though it is simpler to work in terms of private costs (labour related, equipment and service costs) and social costs.[4] The separate identification of social and environmental costs may be required if the Decision Tool software tracks the two separately.

In deriving costs the assumption is made that an operator's costs provide a reasonable and realistic basis from which to derive unit and other costs. The assumption is also made that the cost and operational information required is accessible though due cognisance of how costs are allocated, at what geographical or hierarchical level of the organisation, needs to be taken. In practice each organisation will have its own way of organising and allocating its cost information, however, using the accounting framework outlined in this chapter it is possible to analyse and transpose the data into a format that can be used within the Methodology described in this book. What follows is a description of the way in which the various costs are built up, following a general framework provided by Figures 5.2 to 5.4.

5.2   Derivation of the Costs

5.2.1   Resources and Treatment Costs

This calculates the value of raw water, the cost of abstraction and treatment and supplies this as an at-boundary input cost (Figure 5.5). If the water supply zone is supplied from several different sources then adjustments have to be made to the fixed cost items that are charged.

Cost of abstraction includes the costs of low lift pumping, operation and maintenance of reservoirs and general costs. It is assumed (and this applies for subsequent items as well) that a certain amount of cost data preparation will have been carried out to get costs into the required format. In certain cases it may not be possible to include "Operation and Maintenance" costs as these are booked to a central operations cost centre. In such cases care must be taken to include an appropriate cost element to reflect these costs.

---

[1] Labour related costs covers the gross cost of employment, it includes all associated service related costs such as salaries, bonuses, perks, pension contributions, insurances and any other entitlements.

[2] Materials and Equipment covers the purchase and provision of all materials necessary for remaining in operation such as consumables, office supplies, chemicals, fuel, office equipment, vehicles, machinery and plant.

[3] Services includes the services provided to the operator by third parties that may be contracted out, bought or required from time to time and includes abstraction charges, gas and electricity.

[4] Social costs do not refer to the costs of environmental or water quality related programmes that the operator may be responsible for, nor monitoring of compliance activities. These are operational or capital maintenance activities and should be accounted for in the appropriate categories.

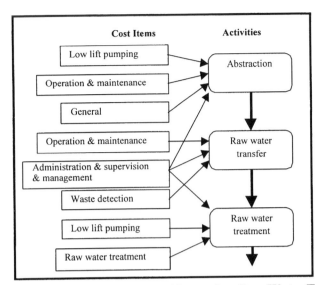

Figure 5.5: Cost Items and Activities in Abstraction, Raw Water Transfer and Treatment

Raw water transfer includes the costs of the operation and maintenance of aqueducts that transfer water from the point of abstraction to the water treatment works and the cost of waste detection activities.

Raw water treatment includes the costs of the low lift pumping, treatment and any other costs pertinent to the running and operation of the various works. Some of the costs associated with the pumping of the treated water may be included here.

Supervision and management associated with Resource and Treatment activities (which have been treated as indirect costs) are included here. The allocation of these costs needs to be carefully considered bearing in mind the hierarchical level at which these costs are attributed and the range of activities the reported costs cover.

5.2.2   Direct Supply: Transfer Costs from Water Treatment to Distribution Input

This cost is made up of two parts: the cost of transferring potable water from treatment works to storage reservoir, and the cost of storing water before it enters a distribution system (Figure 5.6).

Treated water transfer is made up of the costs of high lift pumping and the costs associated with operation and routine maintenance of the transfer mains.

Service reservoirs and towers include the fixed costs associated with the operation and maintenance of these reservoirs as well as the cleaning of the reservoirs. Cleaning is an infrequent activity, occurring once every few years and so an equivalent annual cost should be included.

The activities taken together with the associated administration and supervision costs give the input value of treated water supplied.

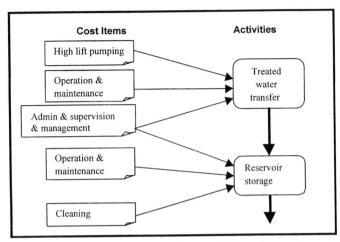

Figure 5.6: Cost Items and Activities in Treated Water Transfer and Reservoir Storage

5.2.3   At-Boundary On-Costs

The resource and treatment together with the direct supply costs identified above constitute the at-boundary on-costs that act as an input cost into the distribution system being considered. Although a way of building up this cost has been suggested, often a supply input cost will be already available. In this case, care must be taken that all the relevant items have been included in the cost supplied.

5.2.4   Distribution

The costs associated within the distribution network, including the at-boundary on-costs need to be allocated to the activities of supply, bursts and leakage. Figure 5.7 provides the activities and cost categories for the costs within the distribution network.

Cost items being allocated to the three cost categories of supply, leakage and bursts are either the direct or indirect cost items (on the left of Figure 5.7) or the hidden cost items (on the right of Figure 5.7). The former are dealt with here, the latter are considered in Section 5.2.5.

The first cost item, located to the far left of Figure 5.7, is that of administration, supervision and management. The work associated with this is spread across a number of items including treated water transfer and storage, waste detection activities, enquiries, complaints, supply related activities and operation and maintenance related activities. The total cost make up of administration, supervision and management must be determined and then allocated across the identified cost items. This allocation may require a best estimate, with the cost split based on duties, time and effort involved for each item.

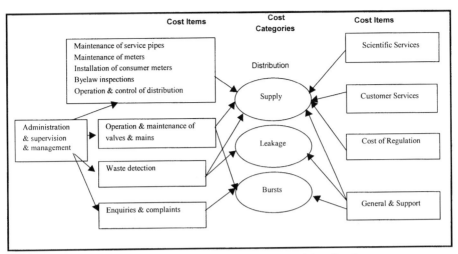

Figure 5.7: Cost Items associated with Distribution

The next item, the top element on second column of Figure 5.7, relates to supply related costs and covers activities such as repair and maintenance of services, byelaw inspections, installation of consumer meters, the operation and control of the distribution of the network. Routine operation and control includes activities such as monitoring of performance, operation of valves, flushing, post treatment etc. These items should include the appropriate portion of administration, supervision and management costs.

The item below this in Figure 5.7 looks at the operation and maintenance activities associated with valves and mains. When considering maintenance it will be necessary to make a differentiation between planned and unplanned actions and then allocate the expenditure accordingly. Planned activities are associated with the normal running and operation of the network, for example regular inspection of mains and valves that occurs year on year. Unplanned activities are associated with non-routine activities associated with structural failures, which are reactive in nature. Whereas, planned maintenance could be construed as fixed, the unplanned expenditure will vary with the number of structural failures within the distribution network. Therefore, it would be advantageous if the unplanned expenditure is reported as a variable cost. Included in the expenditure calculated is the portion of administration, supervision and management costs attributable to the operation and maintenance activities.

The waste detection item includes all activities (use of flow measurement devices etc) associated with detection of wastes, or leakage within the water area, including all associated administration, supervision and management costs. Due to the prevalence afforded leakage in England and Wales, this value has been highlighted. Elsewhere this value should not be as significant.

Last of the items on the left hand side of Figure 5.7, is the cost of the investigation of enquiries and complaints. This cost includes items of expenditure on administration, supervision and management as well as a proportion of the expenditure on business activities. To derive a unit cost per complaint, a breakdown of the number and category of complaints received across the distribution network will need to attained. To attribute these complaints to the three activities of supply, leakage and burst can be achieved through observing the relative breakdown of the source of complaints. It is assumed that complaints arise because of normal supply or as a result of a structural failure or leak. The cost of handling enquiries and complaints is added to this through an analysis of the business activity accounts.

5.2.5 Business Activities

The business activities (consisting of scientific services, customer services, regulation, and general and support activities) support both water supply and sewerage services (see Figure 5.3). It is expected that the reporting of the costs associated with business activities will be high on the hierarchical scale (i.e. company level), with little differentiation between the water and sewerage sides. Where the business activities are not separately accounted for it will be necessary to differentiate the expenditure across the two services to assign costs. An appropriate split may be derived from the total expenditure of activities of the water and sewerage sides at company level. In some instances, for example with scientific service activities, more information will be available to allow an assignment of costs.

Once a value for the business activities has been determined across this large scale, the expenditure then has to be apportioned to the distribution network being considered. At this stage, it may be appropriate to consider for each of the items – customer services, scientific services, regulation, and general and support activities – what the significant cost drivers are in each case. These drivers then can be used as a basis for determination. This will result in a case by case consideration, which itself will serve as a guide as to whether and how some of the costs would need to be allocated between supply, bursts and leakage. For example the costs associated with a call centre would need to be split between supply, bursts and leakage as it is these activities that give rise to the need for a call centre. What is driving the costs (cost driver) and requires resources (and therefore incurs costs) is the number of calls – enquiries, queries and complaints received. An appreciation of this can be used to apportion the total cost associated with the provision of a call centre to the distribution system being considered. In other words consideration has to be given to the appropriate choice of driver or drivers. Some aspects of this procedure are outlined below.

Customer services are predominantly associated with normal supply functions. The number of customers and number of enquiries and complaints are seen as the two principal cost drivers, an analysis of these can be used to allocate the costs to a distribution system. The cost of customer services would be further split between normal water supply operations and dealing with enquiries and complaints. In order to do this a relative split of effort between the two is required, for which number of enquiries and complaints would be an appropriate cost driver.

The cost of scientific services can be handled in a similar fashion to customer services. A distinction between normal supply activities, scientific service tasks that arise out of dealing with complaints and enquiries as well as those related to bursts and other departures from normal operational activities. Depending on the manner in which management costs are kept, it is possible that scientific service costs will be treated as a distinct cost centre and charged out to other parts of an operator's business. Another possibility is that these activities are bought in as a supplied service. If such is the case then great care must be taken to ensure that there is no double accounting.

For simplicity it is suggested that the cost of regulation is wholly attributed to normal supply operations. Identifying suitable cost drivers in this case will be difficult, therefore a simple approach is suggested with the costs being apportioned equally across all the distribution systems.

General and support activity cost items are wholly attributed to normal supply with the exception of three specific items; litigation, public relations, and information and telecommunications. The cost of litigation is separated out as this will be due to a departure from normal conditions and should therefore not be included in such costs. For public relations, a distinction may be made between expenditure on the provision of public relations services and of employee information services. The latter is an internal service for employees whilst the former is required to create and promote an image of the operator in the public sphere. The last item concerns the provision of an information centre and telecommunications. The latter is required to allow the operator to function effectively. The former is a response to the need for information by external bodies, brought about in part by normal operation activities as well as departures from normal operation (the generation of enquiries, requests, complaints and queries). It is thus linked with handling enquiries and complaints. For each cost item an appropriate cost driver has to be determined and used to allocate costs to the distribution system being considered. Opinions as to the most appropriate cost driver and the information available will vary between operators and so each case should be evaluated on its merits. In every case, the allocation of expenditure and resources should be accompanied by a fair and reasonable explanation.

Care should be taken so that costs associated with any capital works are separated out as these are related to the nature and extent of the capital works programme. To include all of these costs under normal operation would create an unbalanced picture. Such costs need to be included in the overall cost of rehabilitation work.

5.3   Consolidating the WLC Accounts

The outline of the derivation of the costs outlined in Section 5.2 was undertaken to develop a suite of costs that represent the three cost categories; supply, leakage and bursts. Section 5.3 details how the various costs introduced in Section 5.2 will appear as entries within a set of WLC accounts. The manner in which the costs are presented here is in keeping with the regulations in England and Wales. However, the inclusion of the costs will not vary greatly from one system to another.

5.3.1   Cost of Supply

The cost of supply brings together all costs associated with normal supply that have been identified and calculated as indicated in Section 5.2. It takes in all the direct and indirect costs, as well as those associated with business activities. Added to them are the incremental risk costs associated with maintaining water quality detailed in Section 4.5.1.13. The risk costs associated with maintaining water quality have been calculated by considering the likely extent of fines and prosecutions and assuming that the operator would seek if possible to avoid incurring these costs. They are broken down into bacteriological, THM (tri-halomethanes), PAH (poly-aromatic hydrocarbons), and discolouration costs.

Table 5.1: Suite of Costs to represent the Supply Cost Category

COST OF SUPPLY	
Cost of water	Cost of customer services
Cost of operation & routine maintenance	Cost of scientific services
Cost of enquiries	Cost of general & support services
Cost to maintain water quality	Image costs
Cost of regulation	

5.3.2   Cost of Bursts

The cost of a burst consists of the direct costs such as repairing a burst plus indirect costs associated with bursts. Indirect costs include: the marginal cost of handling and investigating complaints, the cost of compensation to customers, cost of penalties incurred by the operator. External costs include traffic related congestion costs, value of interruption of supply to customers as well as image (and brand) costs arising from loss of public confidence. The inclusion of these is at the discretion of the operator.

Table 5.2: Suite of Costs to represent the Bursts Cost Category

COST OF BURSTS	
Cost of repairs	Cost of customer services
Cost of operation & routine maintenance	Image costs
Customer compensation	Congestion costs
Regulatory penalties	Disruption to customers
Cost of general & support services	Loss of willingness to pay

The full cost of repair is a function of a number of factors the most significant being location and pipe group characteristics dependent. Included in this should be the costs associated with managerial, administrative and supervisory resources and inputs required to ensure that repairs are initiated and effected efficiently.

The cost of water is ignored here and is included in the cost of leakage.

5.3.3   Cost of Leakage

The cost of leakage is made up of the cost of leakage detection (dependent on the leakage detection strategy adopted), the cost of water lost through leakage (including bursts), the indirect costs and the external costs.

The cost of leakage detection, depends upon the detection strategy adopted and therefore has to be a choice variable of the operator. Other costs associated with the implementation of a leakage control strategy such as the administration, supervision and management costs, enquiries and complaints, and business and support services costs are assumed not to vary with the strategy adopted.

Table 5.3: Suite of Costs to represent the Leakage Cost Category

COST OF LEAKAGE	
Cost of water	Cost of general & support services
Cost of enquiries & complaints	Cost of customer services
Leakage detection strategy costs	Image costs
Regulatory penalties	Loss of willingness to pay

The cost of water lost through leakage is calculated from the input cost of water into the distribution network.

The other costs to include are: cost of penalties and the marginal image cost due to loss of confidence. The cost of rehabilitation programmes aimed at reducing leakage is not included as that would be a management decision and forms part of the Decision Tool.

5.4   Regulatory Penalty Costs

The Methodology relies on penalty costs to maintain performance (or serviceability) within the distribution network at the required level. These include levels of leakage and the serviceability indicators, though they can be associated with any key performance indicator. These penalties constrain the performance in a way analogous to goal programming. However, they have a physical reality in the regulatory framework of England and Wales where companies can be fined, and actions enforced at the companies' expense where serviceability is not maintained. Consistent failure to meet the required levels of serviceability may result in the loss of the operator's license.

The penalty costs suggested are on a sliding scale associated with departures from the regulator's targets and these can be altered to reflect the expected attitude of the regulator. Equally, it provides a mechanism by which an operator can balance the cost savings in not reaching the required levels with the penalties associated with not meeting them. In some cases there is a temporal dimension, for example leakage targets will not be the same over the whole period of analysis and the expected changes need to be reflected.

CHAPTER SIX
Performance Based Cost Drivers I
Supply and Demand

6.1   Introduction

Many of the cost drivers identified in Chapters 4 and 5 are performance based and therefore pragmatic assessment of distribution network performance must be made. Methodologies for this assessment must be able to take in knowledge and data and be able to quantify current and future performance and the effect on performance of interventions. Chapter 6 covers methodologies for the assessment of different aspects of supply and demand for water within a network.

Leakage increases the overall volume of water required to feed a network. Leakage also drives many other costs, for example those associated with leakage control activity. In England and Wales, mandatory leakage levels are set by the economic regulator. Regulatory penalty costs are therefore associated with leakage, which increase progressively where these levels are breached.

The demand for water from customers within the network changes with time, driving the quantity of water coming into the network, and is therefore a major consideration over the period of analysis. The hydraulic capacity of the network may reduce with time as the condition of the bores of especially unlined ferrous mains deteriorate with time and become hydraulically rougher. The combination of increased demand and reduced hydraulic capacity may result in pressure deficiency in areas of a network driving the respective regulatory penalty cost.

6.2   Leakage Performance

6.2.1   Leakage in England and Wales

Leakage can be defined as that water which, having been obtained from a source and treated and put into supply, leaks or escapes other than by a deliberate or controllable action. This water is often referred to as unaccounted for water (UFW) corresponding to the discrepancy between the measured supply of, and measured and projected demand for, water.

Report 26 (NWC/DoE, 1980) advocated the physical disaggregation of distribution networks into district meter areas (DMAs) for leakage control. Implementation took many years and was still underway at the time of privatisation in 1989. At this point much of the understanding of leakage control, both physically (technologically) and economically was still to be developed. The National Leakage Control Initiative (NLCI) reviewed developments with particular focus on the impact that advancements in technology and knowledge, and the regulatory bodies, had had on leakage control policy and practice. The NCLI produced the *"Managing Leakage"* series of reports (UK Water Industry, 1994).

Following privatisation, Ofwat adopted a non-interventionist approach to leakage as they considered that companies had a profit driven incentive to reduce leakage (National Audit Office, 2000). However, within the simulated market conditions created by the regulator, leakage took a low priority with companies' efforts directed elsewhere in the drive to make profits. Until 1995, cost considerations over the economic level of leakage were limited to the marginal cost of treating and distributing the water and the cost of leakage reduction. The possibility of capital deferment through reduced leakage levels was also recognised. However, the 1995 drought brought into public focus the issue of leakage levels against a background of worries over the security of supply and environmental impact. The social value of security of supply and public attitude toward the perceived over use of environmental resources also had to be added into the economic equation. In 1996, Ofwat made some effort to internalise the costs associated with the environmental impact of leakage when companies were asked to quantify economic levels to include environmental considerations. However, these assessments possibly did not reflect the social value of the security of supply and leakage levels were still perceived as high. At this point, rather than tackling the problem from the idea of what levels the companies thought were economic, in 1997, in consultation with the EA, Ofwat began to set company specific mandatory annual leakage targets with which companies must comply or face stringent penalties.

The NAO (2000) recognised that reductions in leakage had produced benefits in increasing headroom. However, they observed that the cost of reducing leakage from its levels in 1995 was unclear and the benefits of capital deferment were also difficult to value. Uncertainty was also recognised in terms of attaching values to the costs and benefits to society and the environment of reduced leakage. The main concern of the NAO in respect of leakage, therefore, was that costs needed to be quantified more robustly such that more confidence could be attached to them.

In summary, the economic equation for leakage is unaccomplished. Although there is wide support, from both companies and regulatory bodies, for the ethos of achieving the economic level of leakage, its calculation is not readily possible. It is arguable that in recent years leakage levels have been driven down by political pressure. The idea of the economic level of leakage is fundamentally flawed in that leakage should not be considered in isolation, especially in view of the holistic performance evaluation aspirations in MD161 (Ofwat, 2000a). In the WLC Methodology, rather than considering the economic level of leakage, the economic level of all appropriate operational variables (to include mains replacement) are considered interactively. The Methodology does not avoid the need for robust values to be attached to the various cost elements. However, with proper identification of the framework of costs and their drivers, the Methodology can be used to evaluate leakage in consideration with all other costs and performance aspects.

6.2.2 Background

By way of a literature review, Skipworth et al. (1999) identified and examined the numerous factors affecting leakage levels and how these factors varied locally. It was argued that it was clearly unreasonable to expect all companies to approach the same level of leakage in view of regional factors. For example, even in the light of recent developments in pressure reduction and control, average network pressure is still significantly constrained by topography. Skipworth et al. (1999) also discussed the influence of, for example, network age, ground and soil type, pipe material and diameter, and density of service connection on leakage levels. The review was by no means exhaustive but provided some background on these issues.

6.2.2.1   *Leakage Control Strategies*

Detection of unreported leaks is invariably carried out at DMA level in two stages;

- *The analysis of minimum night flow (NFM) is carried out routinely to establish whether leakage has increased.* The frequency at which flow data from district meters is downloaded and analysed will dictate the maximum length of time for which unreported leaks are allowed to run, and the effects of this will be reflected in levels of UFW. Telemetry links allow data to be transferred and analysed at any given frequency. In the limit, real time analysis of flow data can be carried out in the interests of leakage control.

- *If leakage has increased sufficiently to warrant further investigation, manual leak detection is carried out.* Leaks are localised or pinpointed via leak noise correlation, step tests or sounding.

Report 26 reported that leakage varied with pressure to the power of 3/2. Pressure reduction is therefore used as a very effective part of many leakage control strategies. The design of pressure reduction schemes is aided by computational network models. Solutions must achieve the fine balance between maintaining the pressure of supply to the customer whilst minimising pressure to minimise leakage.

6.2.2.2   *Pipe Replacement and Leakage*

The consequences associated with ageing pipelines are likely to include increased leakage through seepage and an increased frequency of bursts. Pipe replacement has the potential to reduce water lost via both these mechanisms.

Pipe assets in the UK have commonly suffered comparative neglect. Rehabilitation rates have been far lower than those reported for countries where leakage levels are much lower. For example, Butler and West (1987) stated at the time that in the UK average network age was around 50 years and that average leakage was around 30% of distribution input, an average of 20% under active and 45% under passive leakage control. In their assessment of five companies in Germany and Holland,[1] leakage levels ranged from 2% of distribution input under active to 15% under passive policies. The average age of each network, however, was between 20 and 25 years with accompanying renewal rates of 2 to 3% p.a. Based on this and other evidence (e.g. Aihara and Tateishi, 1994), it is reasonable to assume that one of the benefits of pipeline replacement is a reduction in leakage.

6.2.2.3   *Service Pipe Leakage*

The point of delivery splits the service pipe into the company's communication pipe and the customer's supply pipe. The customer's supply pipe constitutes the length of pipe between the point of delivery, usually the roadside stop tap, and the first point of

---

[1] Leakage levels are reported differently in each country and therefore only broad comparisons are possible.

practicable use inside the building. Although water leaked on supply pipes is considered as water delivered, responsibility for detection and repair of these leaks is incumbent on the water companies. Further, leakage from this component of the distribution system is estimated to contribute significantly to levels of UFW and hence the limit of reducible leakage. For example, Ofwat (2000b) gave figures showing that supply pipe leakage accounted for more than a quarter of overall leakage in England and Wales.

6.2.2.4   *Natural Rate of Rise of Leakage*

The natural rate of rise of leakage (NRR) defines the increase that would take place with time under a passive leakage control policy (as defined in Report 26) where only reported bursts or low pressure complaints are acted upon. The NRR will be dependant on physical variables which describe the individual DMA. Butler and West (1987) estimated that NRR varied between 1 and 4 l/prop/hr/yr with the lower end of the range tending to reflect the presence of newer pipelines. By avoiding carrying out work in some areas, Arscott and Grimshaw (1996) observed a NRR of 2 l/prop/hr/yr. Figures of this order could represent a doubling of leakage year on year at current levels demonstrating the necessity and benefit of leakage control. Also, the relationship between network age and NRR demonstrates that there is a second order effect as NRR is likely to increase year on year. Leakage control activity would therefore have to be intensified year on year to control down leakage by the full amount that equates to its NRR.

As part of the Methodology it is necessary to estimate the NRR for the particular water area (i.e. at DMA or WSZ level). The UKWIR identified the principle determinants of NRR as the length of mains per property, AZNP and asset condition and identified a broad methodology which might be utilised to derive a NRR equation in the form given below in Equation 6.1.

$$NRR = a(Lo)^{b1}(L/N)^{b2}(AZNP)^{b3}(C)^{b4} \qquad (6.1)$$

where, *Lo* is current leakage, *L/N* is metres of main per property, *AZNP* is average zonal night pressure, *C* is asset condition, and *a, b1, b2, b3, b4* are estimated using pilot data. Asset condition was defined *"for example, by pipe age with a weighting for both soil and pipe material"* instead of these factors being broken out as individual determinants. No indication of the dimensions of *C* are given and it is assumed that *a, b1, b2, b3, b4* are dimensionless. Little supporting evidence is given for the form of equation and the model remains unconvincing.

The UKWIR (1999) report highlighted the seasonality of NRR. However, within the WLC Approach, it is the long run NRR which is important, i.e. acting over the period of years. Datasets of nightline with time and accompanying operational data with time (e.g. leakage control activity, AZNP, rehabilitation) should be compiled for areas of different environmental and pipe make up (e.g. soil conditions, diameter, material, age service density). The datasets, which should span a period of years, can be analysed to partition the effect of the time dependant operational variables (see Kleiner and Rajani, 2000, on burst prediction) in order to deduce NRR for a particular DMA. Based on repetitions of this exercise for DMAs of different make up and age, a model could be derived to predict NRR based on DMA description, and the rate of change of NRR with time (defined later as NRR_m' in Section 6.2.4.1).

6.2.3   Economic Level of Leakage

The economic level of leakage has been defined as the level of leakage where the long run marginal cost of leakage control is equal to the long run marginal benefit of the water saved. The diagram in Figure 6.1 has been presented by many authors (e.g. Shore, 1988; Arscott and Grimshaw, 1996; Smith, 1992). Smith (1992) commented that it was the function which defined the effect of the leakage control effort that remained the uncertain component in assessments of the economic attainability of given leakage levels.

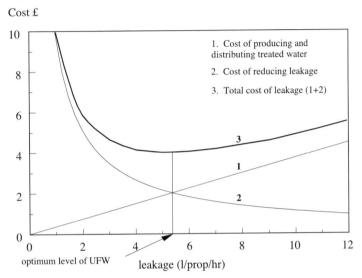

Figure 6.1: The identification of an optimum leakage level based on the economic level of leakage theory

The inappropriateness of this theory within the Methodology was discussed in Section 6.1. Nevertheless, it is recognised within the theory that the appropriate level of leakage will vary between networks and that based on the costs of implementation and of supplying water, the appropriate leakage control policy will vary. Whilst the cost of each method of control may be similar from network to network the benefit of reducing leakage may vary considerably (based on the value of the water entering the network).

6.2.4   Leakage within the Methodology

The cost elements identified in the conventional analysis of leakage levels explained in Section 6.2.1 are appropriate for inclusion in a WLC analysis. However, the economic framework into which they fit must be expanded considerably to reflect the interaction of all other performance aspects (e.g. structural, water quality) and the effect of operational and pipe interventions.

6.2.4.1   Leakage Performance and Performance Relationships

Within the Methodology, leakage is apportioned between SERVICE PIPES and MAINS to reflect current leakage.

For the water area being considered, the function in Figure 6.2 showing percentage mains replacement versus percentage reduction in leakage volume, must be defined given a choice of curve type (e.g. constant, linear, power, polynomial, exponential). This relationship must also be defined for other pipe interventions being considered, i.e. any methods of structural and non-structural relining. No similar relationship is defined for service pipe replacement. Service pipe replacement could be defined as a leakage control strategy.

For the particular water area, NRR must be defined for the mains (NRR_m) and service pipes (NRR_s). The NRR is dependant on the make up of the particular water area (see Section 6.2.2.4), with older networks having higher NRR. The NRR will therefore vary between water areas and with the passage of time, as the age of the network changes, and with mains rehabilitation. For a given water area (of given make up), the user must estimate initial rates, NRR_{mi} and NRR_{si} (l/prop/hr/yr) and a constant $NRR_m{}'$ (l/prop/hr/yr/yr of age) by which NRR_{mi} changes with the average age of the network. This assumes a linear change in NRR_m with average age of the network. Service pipe age is not tracked. The NRR_s, therefore, is assumed to be constant with time.[2] Figure 6.3 demonstrates a simple example of how NRR_m and NRR_s change with time and mains replacement according to this model.

The effect of leakage control strategies on either component of leakage volume (mains and service pipes) must be defined as shown in the example in Table 6.1. This table shows the control strategies, which component of leakage they act on and their effect on reducing leakage (the values in the third column of Table 6.1 are arbitrary).

Table 6.1: Defining the effect of leakage control strategies

Leakage Control Strategy	Leakage component	% reduction of leakage component
Additional Inspection	mains	8
Pressure Reduction	total	20
Detection and Repair Service to Customers	services	2
Normal Leakage Detection (nightline control)	mains	20

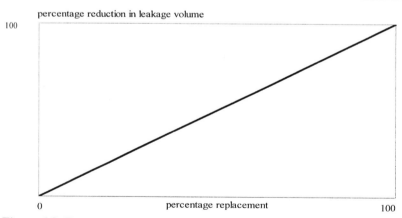

Figure 6.2: Percentage replacement v percentage reduction in leakage volume

---

[2] Leakage at service pipe connection ferrules is captured by mains leakage and in line with the model will reduce as mains are replaced.

NRR (l/prop/hr/yr)

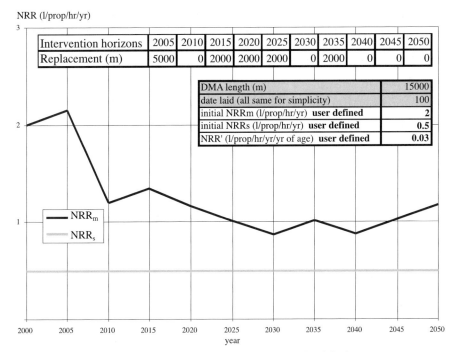

Intervention horizons	2005	2010	2015	2020	2025	2030	2035	2040	2045	2050
Replacement (m)	5000	0	2000	2000	2000	0	2000	0	0	0

DMA length (m)	15000
date laid (all same for simplicity)	100
initial NRRm (l/prop/hr/yr) **user defined**	2
initial NRRs (l/prop/hr/yr) **user defined**	0.5
NRR' (l/prop/hr/yr/yr of age) **user defined**	0.03

NRR$_m$

NRR$_s$

Figure 6.3: Example of change in NRR with time

6.2.4.2   The Effect of Different Rehabilitation Techniques

The model can be extended to account for the effects of different rehabilitation techniques, e.g. structural relining and non-structural relining. A curve similar to that in Figure 6.2 must be defined for each technique.

The NRR model must be extended as shown in Figure 6.4 to account for the effect of each technique. This is done by the application of a set of "NRR impact indices" which act on the effective age of the pipe in the case of an intervention. The NRR is then calculated from the average effective age of the network. Thus, if a technique has an NRR impact index of 0.7 and this technique was used on a 100 year old main, the main's new effective age for the sake of NRR calculation would be 30 years. Hence, the NRR model now accounts for the effect on NRR of the application to pipe lengths in the water area of different techniques at different intervention horizons, and the creep up in NRR with average network age.

NRR (l/prop/hr/yr)

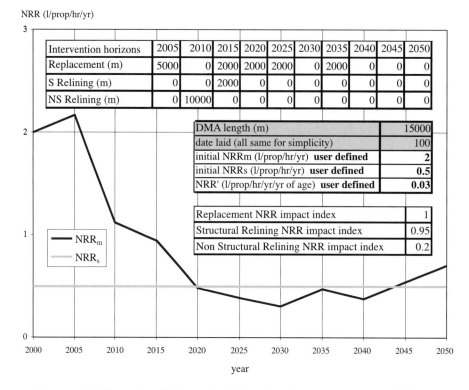

Intervention horizons	2005	2010	2015	2020	2025	2030	2035	2040	2045	2050
Replacement (m)	5000	0	2000	2000	2000	0	2000	0	0	0
S Relining (m)	0	0	2000	0	0	0	0	0	0	0
NS Relining (m)	0	10000	0	0	0	0	0	0	0	0

DMA length (m)	15000
date laid (all same for simplicity)	100
initial NRRm (l/prop/hr/yr) **user defined**	2
initial NRRs (l/prop/hr/yr) **user defined**	0.5
NRR' (l/prop/hr/yr/yr of age) **user defined**	0.03

Replacement NRR impact index	1
Structural Relining NRR impact index	0.95
Non Structural Relining NRR impact index	0.2

year

Figure 6.4: Example of change in NRR with time to account for different rehabilitation techniques

6.3   Demand Patterns and Projections

The geographical distribution, magnitude and daily temporal variation in demand allocated in the building of hydraulic models is estimated based on customer type and number. Demands curves are differentiated by customer type and allocated based on the geographical distribution of customers (the most basic distinction in customer type being domestic/commercial). The hydraulic model component of the "Network Performance" utilises these demands to check the adequacy of the network in its ability to supply them.

In the longer term, over periods of decades, the demand placed on a network will vary due to demographic changes (e.g. occupancy rate, consolidation in existing urban areas, changes in land use) and habitual changes (e.g. increase in per capita consumption). Increases in demand in the long term may affect the ability of a network to fulfil its fundamental function of supplying the required water to customers at satisfactory pressure.

Much literature has originated from the regulators (e.g. EA, 2000 Water Resource Planning Guidelines) that details appropriate methods to project demand into the future. The EA's concern is over environmental impact through increased abstractions, while Ofwat is concerned with the infrastructure that may need to be invested in, in view of the required capacity of fixed assets. Ofwat (2001a) has recognised that marginal costs were forecasts that relied on engineering judgements and that such forecasts were obviously subject to uncertainty. This was said in the context of LRMC (long run marginal cost) calculations, which are heavily reliant on demand projection. Ofwat, however, added the caveat that because of this uncertainty there was a need for clarity about the basis of estimates, as well as an appreciation of the range of uncertainties. When considering an appropriate projection, Ofwat (2001a) made reference to the following;

- Changes in land use
- The effect of the free meter option
- Consideration of any demand management schemes
- Possible savings in the water lost through leakage management (this is dealt with elsewhere in the *Leakage* sub-module)
- Climate change scenarios (guidance in UKWIR, 1997)

It is impossible to stipulate exactly what should be included here due to the variation that exists between companies' assets and resource constraints.

6.3.1 Demand Projections within the Methodology

The distinction is made between accounted for water and that lost due to leakage. The latter is considered within the *Leakage* sub-module. The following only refers to the accounted for water, i.e. the demand placed on the network that will be charged to customers.

The Methodology requires the definition of a relationship to describe the projected increase in demand with time for each water area (e.g. DMA or WSZ). The demands within the hydraulic model are updated for each time period throughout the period of analysis by a factor in accordance with this demand projection curve. Demand types are not differentiated. If this was deemed to be inadequate, the ability to supply a different projection for each demand type could be included.

There is no provision in the Methodology to include demand management schemes as decision variables in the way that the leakage sub-module does in respect of leakage control strategies. It is suggested, therefore, that the demand projection curve should reflect the effects of all demand management schemes either in place or planned. This is referred to by Ofwat (in MD 170) as the *"constrained demand forecast"*. A future development of the Methodology could be to include an unconstrained demand projection sub-module. The demand management schemes could be included as decision variables by assigning the various alternative schemes as interventions whose effect was on the accounted for water. This is analogous to the changes in leakage control strategy and their effect on unaccounted for water.

6.3.2 Security of Supply

Security of supply is a term used in water resource planning with reference to the level of confidence that the volume of the water available for supply can in any event meet the demand of the customers. It is a function of a wide variety of factors including asset capacity (pipes, treatment plants and storage), probable outages, yields, demands and the operational practices in terms of emergency provision. Headroom, which refers to the difference between the water available for use (WAFU) and the demand on the network, is used as a planning tool. If the headroom is below the minimum required, this does not imply that a disruption to supply is imminent. Rather, it implies that the risk of disruption has reached unacceptable levels.

Due to the geographical boundaries placed on the Methodology, security of supply is implied in the costs that are brought in from the "WLC Accounting" module. Headroom does, however, fall under the risk balancing ethos discussed in Section 1.4. It is unlikely that investment directed at improving this level of service would be directed at the distribution network. However, any investment required within the geographical boundaries to ensure appropriate service to the customer is dealt with explicitly within the hydraulic modelling and other performance sub-modules.

6.4   Hydraulic Capacity

A water distribution network is required to satisfy the demand for water at a given pressure head. In England and Wales, the minimum pressure stipulated by Ofwat in their serviceability criteria (DG2) is 15 metres at the customer's side of the service connection. The minimum head required in the distribution mains themselves, therefore, is considered to be 17 metres. The DG2 serviceability measure requires that companies report the percentage of properties that are in danger of receiving a supply below the agreed head.

The hydraulic pressure requirement is generally considered a hard constraint. The WLC accounting approach deals with this directly by attaching regulatory penalties (monetary sums) to DG2 failures. Outside of the regulatory penalty costs there are no other significant costs associated with this aspect of hydraulic performance. Complaints may occur due to low pressure, although it is more likely that these are associated with unusual events such as bursts, the costs of which are accounted for elsewhere in the Methodology. It is unlikely that a consumer, unless new to the network, will complain of low pressure unless there is a change.

The pressure performance of a network may deteriorate with time. This is either due to increases in network demand or the reduction in the hydraulic capacity of the pipes. The former factor is accounted for in the "Demand Projection" sub-module (Section 6.3). The latter is normally associated with internal corrosion of ferrous mains. Predicting rates of corrosion and the build up of semi-permanent deposits on the bores of distribution mains is a complex task. Only a few studies have investigated the deterioration in pipe hydraulic capacity with time. For example, Lamont (1981) and Sharp and Walski (1988) produced tables of typical roughness coefficients for pipes of given material, diameters and ages. Therefore, accurate knowledge of this process of deterioration may be lacking. However, its role as a driver for mains rehabilitation cannot be denied.

6.4.1   The Requirement for a Hydraulic Model within the Methodology

Preparing a calibrated hydraulic model of a water distribution network is a time consuming and expensive task. In addition, the uncertainties in demand allocation, the attributes and properties of the mains, both now and in the future, mean that confidence when utilising them in long term planning is limited. As identified above, only the one cost is associated with hydraulic under-performance and therefore with the complete lack of a calibrated model of the network in question. Hence, it may be decided that the hydraulic consideration of the network be placed outside the Methodology. Such a decision would limit what could be considered within the Methodology. It would exclude consideration of the impact on hydraulic performance of changes in the distribution and magnitude of demand and the pipes' hydraulic roughnesses over time. It would also exclude the possible savings associated with downsizing sections of the network with over capacity and any exhaustive (hydraulic modelling-based) consideration of customer interruptions within the WLC framework (see Section 7.2.2.2). However, excluding the hydraulic model has the advantage of simplifying implementation of the Methodology, particularly in dramatically reducing its computational intensity.

In conclusion, two alternative approaches are available for consideration of the hydraulic performance of the network in question;

• explicit inclusion of the hydraulic performance within the WLC framework,
• consideration of hydraulic performance outside the WLC framework.

6.4.2 Explicit Inclusion of the Network Hydraulic Performance within the WLC Framework

The decision to include the hydraulic model enables all interventions which affect hydraulic capacity to follow the holistic track. An exhaustive approach will include an analysis of the hydraulic performance of the network each time an intervention is made, at each intervention horizon within each optimisation iteration (optimisation is used to automate the Methodology). This dramatically increases the complexity of the problem and limits the choice of algorithms that can be used within the decision tool to search for the optimal management decision scenario to satisfy all performance criteria.

If it is decided that it is necessary to include the hydraulic model, the total interventionary work must be checked to ensure that it meets the hydraulic performance requirements at each intervention horizon. Mathematically, the required performance check is given by,

$$H_{i,t} \geq H_{min} \qquad (6.2)$$

where, $H_{i,t}$ is the head at each location i at time t and H_{min} is the minimum head requirement.

The hydraulic modelling of a water distribution network requires that demands are aggregated at nodes. These demands are normally associated with customer service locations around the node. Equation 6.2 can be used at each demand node to check the number of services that may not receive an adequate supply. This, given the total number of service connections, gives a proxy to the DG2 measure of the percentage of properties that receive a supply below the minimum pressure level. To make this hydraulic analysis more tractable, the hydraulic model can be run for a single snapshot in time (i.e. in steady state) corresponding to peak hour.

Low pressure incidents which are excluded from reporting under the DG2 serviceability measure include those associated with times of abnormal demand or planned maintenance, or one-off incidents of short duration. Up to five low pressure events per year for each property due to demand peaks can be excluded. This can be extended to 25 incidents occurring at any time within a five year AMP period. One-off incidents that can be excluded include pressure loss due to a mains burst, failure of equipment (e.g. pumps), fire-fighting and action by a third party. It can be surmised that the practice of assuming a peak steady state demand when checking the hydraulic capacity of the network is in keeping with these exclusions.

Within the WLC approach, the effects of increases in pipe hydraulic roughnesses with time can be considered through utilisation of empirically derived relationships. Equations can be assigned for each material type and possibly may change for each zone depending on water quality. If the water company does not hold information upon which to base such relationships, they can be derived or estimated by other means, for example from the limited available literature, or a nominal effect can be included.

6.4.3   Consideration of Network Hydraulic Performance outside the WLC Framework

The alternative to the explicit consideration of hydraulic performance within the Methodology is to check hydraulic performance at each intervention horizon following application of the WLC approach, i.e. once the interventions have been finalised. If changes in hydraulic roughness are anticipated with time then this must be incorporated. Care must be taken whenever downsizing occurs (this includes the application of any technique that decreases the internal diameter of the main).

CHAPTER SEVEN
Performance Based Cost Drivers II
Structural Performance

Structural mains failures drive many costs and their level must therefore be quantified and projected into the future based on an understanding of the network behaviour, how this is related to the network's physical description, and how this is likely to change with time. Alternative methods which have been presented in past literature for giving such understanding and prediction are presented and discussed in Chapter 7. A method suitable for analysis of the relatively short duration of data typically available in water companies in England and Wales is presented. This method uses spatial smoothing, drawing information from a wider geographical area for application and adjustment at local level. Network behaviour in relation to the age spectrum of its assets is considered to try to understand the effect of ageing.

Notwithstanding the "burn-in" period following pipe replacement, the benefits of replacement or certain other types of rehabilitation (e.g. structural relining) will include reduced burst rate. A quantification of burst rate related to different pipe descriptive and environmental parameters (e.g. material, diameter, age) will reveal what the likely reduction in burst rate may be for a particular rehabilitation action.

Part of the consequence of structural mains failure is interruption to customers' services. These interruptions drive costs as identified in Chapters 4 and 5 and must therefore be understood and modelled as part of the Methodology. Customer interruptions are considered a sub-set of bursts and are therefore attached to each burst.

7.1   Structural Performance

Within the Methodology, there is the need to quantify the likely future number of structural mains failures and their distribution across the pipe asset base. The number of future events cannot be ascertained with absolute certainty but an estimation can be derived from historical failure data. A characteristic failure rate can then be attached to each length of pipe based on its asset and environmental description.

A main fails when its residual strength becomes inadequate to resist the forces imparted on it. The strength of the main and the rate of deterioration in its ability to resist forces is a function of pipe descriptive and environmental attributes. In terms of *long term failure behaviour*, therefore, it can be considered that over the service life of a main its propensity to burst depends on fixed parameters such as material, diameter, density of services and soil properties.

Ultimately, a main fails in response to the total load momentarily exceeding its load bearing capacity. In terms of *short term failure behaviour* and fluctuations in burst rate in a given geographical area, the balancing factors are either meteorologically or operationally driven. Ground movement and the temperature gradients set up across pipes due to changes in, for example, water temperature have been shown to be driven by meteorological variations which take place over the periods of weeks/months (Skipworth et al., 2000; Habibian, 1994). Operationally, bursts may take place due to high network pressure (Pascal and Revol, 1994) or pressure transients that result from, for example, pump or valve operation.

Analyses upon which to base investment in maintenance of the distribution network are done over time horizons of decades. It is therefore the *long term failure behaviour* which is relevant to the Methodology.

In broad terms, in respect of the analysis of long term failure behaviour, two options are available to derive the change in burst rate with mains age. Firstly, where good long term historical records are available going back a number of decades, direct analyses can be carried out whereby the effects of, for example, rehabilitation are separated from the long term increase in burst rate (e.g. Kleiner and Rajani, 2000). Secondly, however, where the extent of available burst data is much less and confidence in asset data is low, other, less direct methods must be used. Typically, the data available for water companies in England and Wales falls into this second category.

7.1.1   Background

Fundamentally, the two primary mechanisms behind mains bursts are the physical deterioration that occurs to the mains materials (Section 7.1.1.1) and the loading that will ultimately cause the main to fail structurally (Section 7.1.1.2). However, to model these deterministically is practically impossible. With an appreciation of the mechanisms, however, proxies of the pipe descriptive and environmental factors affecting mains failure (Section 7.1.1.3) can be used in the development of models to estimate future failure rates. Such models are discussed in Section 7.1.1.4.

7.1.1.1   Deterioration of a Water Main

Depending on the main's material type, physical deterioration is primarily due to corrosion. Chemical interaction occurs both internally with the mains water and externally with the surrounding environment.

The corrosion of metallic (ferrous) water mains is largely due to the potential difference between two areas on the surface of the metal which creates the elements of a cell, i.e. an anode and a cathode. The metal itself provides an electrical conductor and either the mains water internally, or the interstitial soil water externally, provides an electrolyte. There are four main types of corrosion that are of interest in water distribution networks; uniform, localised, galvanic and concentration cell corrosion (AWWARF, 1996). External corrosion is primarily galvanic (O'Day, 1989) whereby a current is created between the main and the soil. The properties of the soil (e.g. the soil's resistivity, pH, redox potential and moisture content) will determine the amount of external corrosion that will occur. In the case of internal corrosion a cell is created on the bore of the main with the transported water and its constituents acting as the electrolyte. Internal corrosion is not as structurally damaging as external corrosion and as such is not given much attention in the literature.

Cement based mains may also undergo a degenerative chemical reaction internally and externally. The overall process is a chemical as opposed to an electrochemical reaction. The reaction involves the leaching out of the CaO, the binding constituent of the cement matrix. In the case of external corrosion this will occur in high sulphide content soils and in some cases there will be a drastic effect on the main's structural integrity. As with metallic mains, the internal effect is less damaging and leaching will only occur if the carbon dioxide/calcium carbonate equilibrium of the transported water is unbalanced.

7.1.1.2 *The Loading on Water Mains*

7.1.1.2.1 Internal Loads

A water main must be able to withstand the pressure exerted by the water that passes through it under normal operational conditions. However, greater pressures are created during surge events caused by, for example, pump switching, valve operation, or simply the sudden imposition of a large customer demand. Surge events have the potential to cause failure by exposing vulnerable parts of the network, sometimes repeatedly, to excessive pressures. The magnitude and duration of pressure surges caused by network events will depend on the nature and origin of the event, the network geometry (pipe diameters, lengths, network connectivity) and the elasticity of the pipe materials which make up the network. It is common practice in the water industry to implement operating policies that minimise the severity of these surge events. These policies include using "soft" or stepped starts for pumps and the use of protocols to ensure gradual opening and closing of valves.

In a circular pipe, the circumferential (hoop) stress due to internal pressure is equal to $Pd/2t$ where P is the pressure in the main, d is the internal diameter and t is the thickness of the main wall. The ability of the main to resist the stress will depend on the material's bursting tensile strength and in corroded mains, the amount of material remaining. The ability of weakened joints to resist the stress may also be important. Small diameter mains are only likely to fail due to circumferential stress if they are heavily corroded but are more likely to fail due to their inability to resist bending, or due to perforation where corrosion is severe.

7.1.1.2.2 External Loads

The external loads that a main experiences will primarily be determined by the surrounding environment. The soil, meteorological conditions and the overlying land use all contribute in determining the magnitude and pattern of loading.

External loads include those associated with the surrounding media and those superimposed from the overlying land use. The most identifiable of these superimposed loads is traffic loading. The main will also have to resist loads created by any differential movement in the soil. Two main causes of soil movement are changes in the moisture content and the heave associated with frost penetration.

Ideally a main is laid such that continuous support is provided by the underlying soil. However, often this continuous support is not provided in the initial installation or is disturbed throughout the lifetime of a main. This disruption can occur due to differential movement in the soil, disturbances by third parties or leaking water. The lack of continuous support leads to the main acting as a beam and the creation of bending stresses.

The ability of the main to resist bending stresses induced by, for example, soil movement or beam action, is a function of the material strength (primarily tensile) and the second moment of area of the main's cross-section which may change with time. The relationship between load and diameter, and second moment of area and diameter is such that mains are much more able to resist bending as diameter increases even if the wall thickness remains constant.

7.1.1.3   *Pipe Descriptive and Environmental Factors Affecting Mains Failure*

The discussions presented in the preceding sections have highlighted the numerous and complex interactions that must be captured in modelling mains failure. Although these interactions are well known, the practical development and application of truly deterministic models is precluded by the huge data requirement which will undoubtedly remain unfulfilled.

This has led to the statistical analysis of historical burst data in order that the complex interactions that lead to mains bursts may be rationalised. Many analyses of this type have been undertaken throughout the world in attempts to find the influence of pipe descriptive and environmental factors on failure rate. The numerous and wide ranging factors that influence mains bursts and the current lack of understanding of how these interact, has led to contradictory findings in these studies. Therefore, controversy still remains on the exact influence on mains bursts of many of the factors.

Due to the sheer number of studies, and because many are based on sensitive company data, there is difficulty in compiling a truly exhaustive review. Many studies consider the influence of environmental factors on leakage levels as well as the frequency of burst events. Often leakage levels are generalised in terms of background losses and bursts. Some crossover in the following sections, therefore, is inevitable although an attempt has been made to concentrate on the influence of different factors on burst frequency.

7.1.1.3.1   Pipe Age

The consequences associated with an ageing pipeline may include an increase in burst frequency. Although it has been found in a number of studies that age alone is a bad indicator of the likelihood of pipe failure (Herbert, 1994; Dyachkov, 1994; O'Day, 1982), Walski (1987a) noted that age plays an important role in determining the attributes which affect the burst life of a main. Age tells the length of time that the main has been in operation, exposed to the surrounding environment, and the time it has been subject to both internal and external loads. However, the ageing effects in one environment will not be the same as those in another.

In some cases, studies have found definite links between age and an increase in burst rate. For example, Kettler and Goulter (1985) found a strong correlation between the age of an asbestos cement main and its burst rate. In their study, Pascal and Revol (1994) found that the number of breaks in cast-iron pipes increased with age.

Age can also give an indication of the design and construction practice used for the main, plus the quality and strength of the material itself. For example, Severn Trent Water found that mains laid since 1950 had much higher break rates than those laid in the earlier part of the century. Similarly, a study carried out at the MIT found that mains laid in the fifties and sixties were less reliable. Both these studies were reported in O'Day (1982).

With regard to plastic mains, the effect of age on burst rate remains difficult to assess due to the relatively short time that these have been in use in the water industry and the relatively small amount that is operational.

7.1.1.3.2   Pipe Material

Because of the material properties, mains will suffer structural failure via different modes. Different seasonal patterns of failure are seen (Skipworth et al., 2000) as the conditions prevail for these different modes of failure to occur.

Many water distribution networks in UK Victorian cities were constructed using cast-iron pipelines. Today, many of these pipes are still in operation and many urban networks are comprised predominantly of such pipes. Many authors have noted the problems associated with ageing cast-iron pipes, in particular their propensity to burst (e.g. Bocock, 1997; Lackington and Burrows, 1994; Pascal and Revol, 1994). The corrosion and embrittlement that occurs with age makes these mains more susceptible to failure than mains of other materials. The ability of small diameter cast-iron mains to accommodate bending, and therefore differential ground movement, is low compared to more ductile metallic mains (e.g. ductile iron, steel) and plastic which have higher elasticities.

7.1.1.3.3   Pipe Diameter

Many studies have highlighted that smaller diameter mains suffer higher break rates. Andreou and Marks (1986) and the US Army Corps of Engineers (reported in Walski et al., 1986) found that smaller diameter mains were more likely to fail due to circumferential cracks and hole blowouts, indicating lack of bending strength and their susceptibility to corrosion. A study undertaken by Ciottoni (1983) also noted the inverse relationship between break rate and diameter. Based on these findings, Kettler and Goulter (1985) undertook a statistical analysis that showed a strong correlation between the average break rate and mains diameter for data collected in Winnipeg, Canada. In some cases, the correlation showed an almost linear inverse relationship between average break rate and diameter. However, the strength of the correlation was found to be a function of pipe material. For example, there was a strong correlation found for cast-iron mains, but no such relationship was found for asbestos cement mains.

The inverse relationship between break rate and mains diameter has also been recognised in the modelling approaches to break rate prediction of Shamir and Howard (1979) and Walski and Pelliccia (1982). These are discussed in Section 7.1.1.4.

7.1.1.3.4   Traffic Loading

Francis (1994) suggested that the ground movement which caused bursts was often attributable to traffic loading. However, in an analysis of burst data corresponding to a seven year period in the town of Bagnolet, France, Pascal and Revol (1994) found that there was no correlation between bursts and traffic density and the position of the pipe. Although Marshall (1999) did not attempt to correlate traffic loading with burst data, it was found via detailed measurements that long term loading levels from soil and traffic were far less than those predicted by standard UK design procedures for light traffic. They also found that the response of fill to dynamic traffic loading was elastic and there was no permanent increase in external pressure on the pipe or any pipe deformation.

7.1.1.3.5   Ground Type

Ground movement may be caused by a number of factors, introducing additional stresses to pipes, which may cause fatigue or ultimately failure. Soils, for example clays, can be susceptible to heave caused by frost action and shrinking and swelling with changes in moisture content. Soils may also be corrosive to mains. For example, Greek (1997) cited an estimate that a quarter of the UK supply network was laid in highly aggressive and/or shrinkable soil and that there was strong evidence that mains bursts caused by corrosion and fracture correlated with soil factors.

Tsui and Judd (1991) found that 30% of cast-iron mains that had been assessed in their study had failed due to corrosion. They found that the majority of these failures occurred in highly aggressive soils, and that no other explanation for a large proportion of these failures had been recorded. Tsui and Judd also speculated that in many cases, the shrink/swell characteristics that are prevalent in highly aggressive soils may also have been a contributing factor. By observing plots of burst events on soil corrosivity maps, Jarvis and Hedges (1994) concluded that the maps provided a sound basis for partitioning the pipes into areas of equal corrosion risk. Grau (1991) cited the use of soil maps not only for highlighting areas where the burst risk was increased, but also to aid the decision on which material to use for replacement mains.

7.1.1.3.6   Meteorological Conditions

As observed earlier, it is the long term failure behaviour of mains which is relevant in the Methodology. The climate of a particular area will impact on the frequency of burst inducing meteorological conditions to take place.

The failure of brittle pipes (e.g. cast-iron) has often been linked to weather conditions. Precipitation and air temperature influence soil moisture content and ground temperature and in turn ground movement resulting in extra superimposed loading. Air temperature also influences water temperature.

Based on the evidence of Marshall (1999), Habibian (1994) and Skipworth et al. (1999, 2000), water temperature is unlikely to be responsible for short term increases in burst rate in response to short spells of cold weather. However, its longer term variation, which is a function of longer term changes in air temperature, may affect burst rate. This was borne out by the work of Skipworth et al. (2000) who successfully used learning based computational techniques to link precipitation and air temperature data corresponding to the previous two months to burst rate in a predictive model for a given geographical area. The process regression in Figure 7.1 demonstrates the link between these fundamental variables and mains bursts.

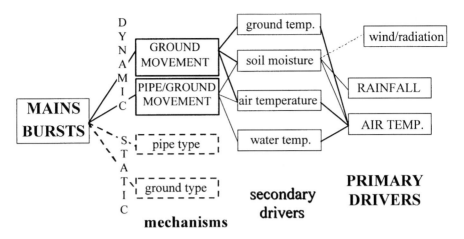

**Figure 7.1: Process regression for temporal failure behaviour of distribution
mains**

Frost action takes place over a time period which corresponds to the period of
sustained cold weather which provokes increased burst rate. The potential of sub-zero
temperatures to induce these short term effects will depend on the moisture content of
the soil and prevailing ground temperature, which will depend on recent (over the
period of the previous weeks) historical meteorological conditions.

7.1.1.3.7   Pressure

The strong link between pressure and leakage levels has been demonstrated (Report
26, NWC/DoE, 1980). The link between pressure levels and burst rate is less certain.
Although minimum feasible operating pressures are still significantly constrained by
local topography (Lambert, 1998), average and residual pressures have reduced in
hilly areas due to pressure management schemes. However, prior to this, residual
pressures may have been considerable and may have caused irreversible damage to
the pipework infrastructure, resulting in increased background leakage and burst rate.

Section 7.1.1.2.1 highlighted the role that pressure surge events play in increasing
stresses in the main's walls that will ultimately expose weak points and cause mains
failure. Built-up areas are likely to suffer the effects of surge due to the number of
instantaneous demands, valve operations and general network activity which take
place. However, there is little published work on the role of pressure surge events in
the occurrence of mains bursts.

7.1.1.3.8   Burst History

A number of authors have noted the temporal relationship between sequential burst
events on the same main. Clark et al. (1982) found that beyond the first failure on a
main, the number of failure events increased exponentially with time. Similarly, for
mains with diameter greater than 200 mm, Andreou and Marks (1986) found that the
time to the next break decreased as each break occurred.

Pipe failures have been seen to occur in the vicinity of and soon after previous burst
repairs. This may be attributable to damage caused by the previous event or the
disturbance caused by the previous repair, e.g. the shock of recharge (Conroy and

Hall, 1995). From data corresponding to mains' breakages in Winnipeg, Canada, Goulter and Kazemi (1988) found that 22% of failures occurred within a metre of a previous failure, and 46% within 20 metres of another failure. Further, they found that 46% of the failures that occurred within a metre of another failure occurred within one day of the previous failure. A number of explanations were suggested for such occurrences including the soil movement caused by the changing moisture content from the leaking water, and the change in thermal conditions with the exposure of the soil to the extreme cold of the air. A further suggestion was that the disturbance to the bedding during a previous repair could cause further local failures.

7.1.1.4   *Modelling Mains Bursts*

7.1.1.4.1   Aggregated and Multiple Regression Type Models

Many burst models are based on an analysis relating environmental and pipe descriptive variables to the recorded burst behaviour resulting in the assignment of bursts per unit length per unit time to a main or group of mains.

Shamir and Howard (1979) aggregated mains into homogenous groups, based on, for example, equivalent diameter, material and age, such that a burst history plot could be obtained for each group. Regression analysis was then applied to obtain the exponential relationship, given as Equation 7.1, between age and the burst rate

$$\lambda(t) = \lambda(t_0)e^{A(t-t_0)} \qquad (7.1)$$

where, t_0 is the base year of the analysis, $\lambda(t_0)$ is the number of bursts/year/1000ft at time t_0 and A is the growth rate coefficient (1/year), with A in the range of 0.05–0.15 depending on the pipe material and diameter.

Clark et al. (1982) identified and modelled two distinct time periods in the burst history of a main. An equation was derived which gave the time lag to the first event, then an exponential equation similar to Equation 7.1 was utilised to describe subsequent burst behaviour. Variables such as main diameter, internal pressure, main type, overlaying land use and the soil type were included in the model of Clark et al. Walski et al. (1986) also utilised an exponential based equation to model burst rate in a similar fashion. Likewise, Mavin (1996) used an exponential type function to model bursts where the entire burst history was known. Where only a partial knowledge of the burst history was available, Constantine and Darroch (1995) utilised a power function of the form,

$$N(t) = at^b \qquad (7.2)$$

where, $N(t)$ is the number of failures and t is the age of the asset. The value for b was obtained from Equation 7.3 which reflects the failure time history.

$$b_i = \frac{N}{\sum_i \sum_j \log \frac{T_i}{t_{ik}}} \qquad (7.3)$$

where, N is the total number of failures, T_i is the age of the ith asset, t_{ik} is the kth failure time of the ith asset. The value of b was found to be approximately equal to 2 for a sub-network in Melbourne and was constant regardless of mains type. The value of a was special to each main. The value of a for main i, a_i, can be calculated by,

$$a_i = \exp\left(\sum_k \mathbf{x}_{ik} \mathbf{e}_k \right) \tag{7.4}$$

where, k denotes a set of environmental factors, x_{ik} is a vector describing the asset and environmental variables and e_k is a vector of regression coefficients.

The models which have been described have commonly been developed where networks have large amounts of reliable asset and burst history data. In most cases, this failure data must be tied to individual mains and must cover periods within which significant degradation has taken place to effect an increase in failure rate, i.e. decades. If such a large data set does not exist it may be difficult to obtain a time dependent relationship for individual mains via these methods.

7.1.1.4.2   Survival Type Models

Survival type models differ from those discussed in Section 7.1.1.4.4 in that they use a probabilistic approach. This assumes that either the "useful life" (with some kind of definition of this) of the pipe or the time to the next failure is a distributed random variable. If the probability distribution of this random variable is known then a survival function can be defined. A survival function gives the percentage of mains that have either not experienced a burst or are viable components at a given time. This will then allow estimation of the failure rate at any time, the expected time to failure, or the "useful life" of a main. These models use regression analyses to find the relationship between the environmental variables and the probability of failure. There are two main forms of the regression model – the Cox-proportional hazard model and the accelerated lifetime model. For example, based on data collected in the US, Andreou et al. (1987) found that the time between failures decreased for each burst up to the third one after which it was constant. To describe the behaviour in the early stages of deterioration up to the third break, a Cox-proportional hazard model, which considered covariates dependent on the network's characteristics (burst history, intrinsic properties and exogenous variables) was used. In the latter stages of deterioration, because of the constant failure rate, a Poisson distribution can be used to obtain the probability that a main will fail during a time period. Andreou et al. (1987) used a regression analysis of burst data to define the probability distribution. They found that the necessary burst history data for such an analysis was not available in most water authorities. In a later study, Tsui and Judd (1991) reached the same conclusion. Lei and Sægrov (1998) and Herz (1996) used accelerated lifetime models to model the time to first failure. Again, the data requirements were unrealistic if any meaningful answer was to be derived.

7.1.2   Modelling Burst Behaviour within the Methodology

It is necessary within the Methodology to estimate the rate of future mains failure based on the description of the mains and failure events which are available in asset databases. There is also a major interest in predicting how failure rate will grow with time. By linking asset information and recorded failure data, models to describe failure rate and the growth in failure rate based on pipe descriptive and environmental parameters should be possible.

Section 7.1.2 and its sub-sections describe the derivation and application of such a model. Any method of analysis is limited by the extent, quality and configuration of data. Hence, the detailed method presented herein is derived with a focus on what data is typically available within water companies in England and Wales and in mind of the evidence presented in Section 7.1.1.3 and the modelling techniques reviewed in Section 7.1.1.4.

7.1.2.1   *Available Data and Analysis Style*

Over the last century, the water industry in the UK has been through many forms of ownership and has been geographically and operationally aggregated and disaggregated in different ways up until privatisation in 1989. Thus, the quality and completeness of the records that the privatised utilities inherited was such that knowledge of the underground assets, in terms of, for example, pipe age, material, diameter and, even, position, was scant for large proportions of their networks. Since privatisation, data has been collected and studies have been carried out in an effort to compile improved asset records. However, some data, such as date laid, is irrecoverable and data to describe diameter and material may not be economic or feasible to collect or derive with certainty. The quality of the data, therefore, remains inevitably compromised due to the pre-privatisation legacy.

Systems are in place to record network activity, including mains bursts. This failure data seldom goes back many years at a reasonable level of quality and completeness and is seldom tied to individual mains. The data has been primarily collected for regulatory purposes and in combination with the asset data does not lend itself easily to being analysed using the techniques outlined in the preceding sections, which have strict and exhaustive data requirements. Given the nature, availability and reliability of data held by water companies in England and Wales, currently it is difficult to see anything but aggregated models being realistically used to understand and estimate future failure rates.

Pipes fail infrequently and relationships which link their occurrence with pipe descriptive and environmental parameters, therefore, are difficult to derive. However, where large water company asset and failure databases exist comprising tens of thousands of kilometres of pipes and tens of thousands of pipe failures stretching over a number of years, analysis based on homogeneous pipe sets can be carried out. The GIS (geographical information system) and database software applications offer the ideal platform upon which to compile, link and interrogate large data sets using the power of modern computers. Water companies worldwide commonly store asset and network activity data on corporate GIS and database software for operational and regulatory purposes.

7.1.2.2   *Recommended Analysis Method*

The method outlined herein is based on the analysis of homogeneous pipe groups and failure data corresponding to these groups. Shamir and Howard (1979) presented an equation similar to that given by Equation 7.5 for the analysis of homogeneous pipe groups.

$$\lambda_i(t) = \lambda_i(t_0)e^{A_i(t-t_0)} \qquad (7.5)$$

where, t_0 is the base year of the analysis,

$\lambda_i(t)$ is burst rate/unit time per unit length at time t for the ith pipe group,

$\lambda_i(t_0)$ is burst rate/unit time per unit length at time t_0 for the ith pipe group,

A_i is the growth coefficient (reciprocal of time) for the ith pipe group, obtained from regression analysis.

Considering the burst rate at time t_0, $\lambda_i(t_0)$, this can be equated as in Equation 7.6.

$$\lambda_i(t_0) = \prod_k \mathbf{x}_{ik} \mathbf{r}_{ik} \tag{7.6}$$

where, k is a set of pipe descriptive and environmental factors,
x_{ik} is a vector describing the pipe descriptive and environmental variables for the ith pipe group,
r_{ik} is a vector of regression coefficients corresponding to these variables.

Equation 7.6 is suitable for the analysis of pipes at a large geographical (i.e. company) level where regression analysis is used to find the coefficients in r_{ik}. However, when Equation 7.6 is applied at local level and the benefits of spatial smoothing disappear, local adjustments must be made, most probably by pipe group. The factor K_i, in Equation 7.7, is a local adjustment factor for pipe group i.

$$\lambda_i(t_0) = K_i \left[\prod_k \mathbf{x}_{ik} \mathbf{r}_{ik} \right] \tag{7.7}$$

Substituting Equation 7.7 into Equation 7.5 gives Equation 7.8, the form of burst model to be used in the burst analysis to derive burst rates for homogeneous pipe groups, and the growth in these factors, for use in the WLC approach.

$$\lambda_i(t) = K_i \left[\prod_k \mathbf{x}_{ik} \mathbf{r}_{ik} \right] e^{A_i(t-t_0)} \tag{7.8}$$

7.1.2.2.1   Limitations of the Analysis Method

The chosen method of analysis is based on homogeneous pipe groups. In order to derive the regression coefficients in r_{ik} and the values for A_i, it is necessary to break the asset and failure databases down by furthering degrees into similar groups as the number of parameters considered is extended. For example, in the analysis presented in Section 7.1.2.3, the asset database is broken down firstly by material, then diameter, then by a parameter describing the degree of urbanisation, and also by age. Even with very large databases comprising tens of thousands of kilometres of main, at some point, the pipe groups and the number of burst events corresponding to these pipe groups become so small that the analysis effectively collapses.

An assumption which is implied by this method of analysis is that when the asset database is broken down into similar pipe groups in consideration of a given variable, the other influential parameters remain evenly distributed across the groups. In the networks under consideration in the UK, this assumption is valid to a sufficient degree to allow this type of analysis. However, as progressively more variables are considered the validity of the assumption decreases. As the analysis progresses, the assumption can be easily tested using database queries. It is, however, a further reason why the number of variables must be limited and has led to the partitioning of parameters into *"accounted for"* and *"unaccounted for"* variables.

7.1.2.2.2   Accounted for and Unaccounted for Variables

Preceding sections of this chapter, give an appreciation of the large number of variables which impact on the propensity of mains to fail and therefore the range of factors which could be included in k, the set of pipe descriptive and environmental factors included in the model described by Equation 7.8. However, given the limitations of the analysis method outlined in Section 7.1.2.2, and the practical and economic implications of collecting extraneous amounts of data, the analysis must be limited to a reasonable number of the most representative influential variables.

The variables which are dealt with explicitly in the company wide analysis are termed *accounted for* variables. The effect of *unaccounted for* variables is rationalised in the application of the model to calculate failure rates for mains in a given area of a distribution network. This procedure effects spatial smoothing whereby information is brought to bear from a wider geographical area for application and adjustment at local level.

The reasons for selection of the *accounted for* variables in the example analysis are discussed in Section 7.1.2.3.

7.1.2.3   Data Requirements

Asset and failure data and data detailing DMA configuration are linked in the analysis. This data is described in the following sections with reference to what is typically available in water companies in England and Wales.

The *accounted for* variables (corresponding to k in Equation 7.8) on which the example analysis is based and which are recommended for use in other analyses are;

    pipe material
    pipe diameter
    density of services scaled by pipe length
    pipe age

The susceptibility of pipes to succumb to failure via loads imposed by, for example, pressure, surge, traffic loading, meteorologically induced ground movement, will be a function of pipe material and diameter. The ability of a pipe to resist failure under loads which induce bending is a function of material properties and second moment of area. These properties may change with age, for example as material is corroded away or suffers embrittlement, and therefore age is included in the model. The effect of age is also used to project the change in failure rate into the future.

The effect on failure rate of the density of services (scaled by mains length) has been used as a surrogate for the degree of urbanisation and to reflect the spatial density of potential weak points in the network (increased concentration of service connections, pipe junctions, valves, joints etc). The degree of urbanisation will dictate the traffic loading, and the frequency of pressure transients resulting from instantaneous demands and other network activity.

So, although parameters such as the degree of corrosion and embrittlement, the ability to resist bending, the spacing of joints, surge, traffic loading and ground movement are not included explicitly as *accounted for* factors, their effect in ultimately inducing failure is considered through inclusion of proxies.

Given the list of variables accounted for in the analysis (pipe diameter, material, age, density of services), this implies that the explicitly *unaccounted for* variables include, for example, pressure and soil conditions.

7.1.2.3.1   Asset Data

The analysis detailed herein is only suitable for application to pipe databases covering in the order of tens of thousands of kilometres.

In water companies in England and Wales, distribution mains are typically catalogued on GIS/databases. Core information is material, diameter, position (start and end node grid references), length and date laid.

For the purpose of the analysis, it is necessary to assign pipes to geographical or operational areas. The DMAs are suitable for this purpose. If pipes are not already assigned in this way then this assignment must be carried out, most probably by overlaying the pipes and DMA boundaries in GIS software.

In summary, for the purpose of the analysis it is necessary to have the distribution pipes catalogued in a database. **The essential information required for each pipe is material, diameter, length, year laid and position (DMA).**

As discussed earlier, asset information may have been incomplete at the time of privatisation. Since then, the water companies in England and Wales have carried out extensive survey work to establish their asset databases. Nevertheless, a significant proportion of the data has remained irrecoverable. Date laid and even material and diameter may be implied via urbanisation contours and/or rules to reflect what materials and pipe diameters were laid in which situations and areas at different times during the evolution of the networks.

7.1.2.3.2   Failure Data

Network activity is recorded in databases. The best record of mains failures comes from stored catalogues of mains repairs. This analysis has been designed around the core information which these catalogues usually contain. **In respect of each recorded repair the information required for the analysis is essentially diameter, material and position (DMA).**

An indication of the age of the failed main and the service density in its vicinity is also required but is implied via the asset information. It is unusual for the position of the events to be stored to an accuracy which allows them to be tied to individual mains. This is not important for the analysis, the method of which has been configured with this fact in mind. The burst (mains repair) event needs to be assigned to a DMA and location information is commonly of sufficient accuracy to allow this. Again, events can be assigned by overlaying the events and DMA boundaries in GIS software and exporting the database with this new field of information. Assigning events in this way allows a representation of the age of the main on which the repair took place and the density of services in the vicinity to be attached to the event.

As the pipe data set is broken down by furthering degrees into homogeneous groups, the corresponding number of burst events must remain significant. This is why the analysis requires large pipe and failure data sets. For the failure data set to contain this amount of data, the data set must span a sufficient time period. It must also be long enough so that extreme failure inducing meteorological events are not significant and a long term average is represented. However, what is actually required for the analysis is a "static" sample of network structural failure behaviour. Ideally, this would mean that during the time period which the failure data set spanned there was consistency in the network such that there was;

(a)   no degradation of the network,

(b)   no rehabilitation of the network, and

(c)   no change in the operation and maintenance strategy.

Of course these ideals are not truly achievable. However, if the time period was short enough in comparison to a mains service life, and rehabilitation rates are low then the first two ideals could be approached. Operation and maintenance strategies have changed over the period since privatisation. Although these changes may have altered the number of mains repaired with time (e.g. increased find and fix), they are unlikely to have changed the distribution of bursts across the variables considered in the analysis (pipe material, pipe diameter, density of services scaled by pipe length, pipe age).

To some extent, such things as those discussed in the above paragraph are *unaccounted for* variables and these are taken care of when models are effectively calibrated to take account of *unaccounted for* variables.

With all things considered, in the example analysis in Section 7.1.2.4, a period of five years corresponding to the latter half of the 1990s was chosen for the timespan of the failure data set.

7.1.2.3.3   Operational Structure

The analysis requires the number of properties in each DMA to be known. The length of mains in each DMA can be found from the asset database and from these two pieces of information the average service density can be found in each DMA.

Age characteristics of the pipe groups within the DMAs can also be distilled. Digitised DMA boundaries can be brought into a GIS and each main and failure event can be associated with service density and age as discussed in Sections 7.1.2.3.1 and 7.1.2.3.2.

7.1.2.3.4   Other Data

Water companies may hold or have access to other data, for example relating to pressure (e.g. average zonal night pressure (AZNP)) or soil properties (e.g. corrosivity, fracture potential). These are *unaccounted for* variables within the method but may be considered more explicitly in studies beyond the type outlined herein.

7.1.2.4   Example Analysis

An analysis of burst and asset data is necessary in order to find the regression coefficients represented by r_{ik} and A_i in the model (Equation 7.8). The operational structure data is used to relate certain variables in the analysis. The best way to demonstrate the chosen analysis method is via an example. Section 7.1.2.4 and its sub-sections, therefore, are written with reference to an example of the application of the method.

In this example, the asset database comprised more than a third of a million pipe lengths totalling around 30 000 km, broken down into around 2000 DMAs. The failure database corresponded to a five year period from 01/01/1995 and contained tens of thousands of mains repair events. Five materials represented over 98% of the water company's distribution network by length and the analysis was therefore limited to these. The five materials were cast iron (CI), ductile iron (DI), asbestos cement (AC), medium density polyethylene (MDPE), and polyvinyl chloride (PVC).

NOTES

1. Units of diameter may be mixed, i.e. in inches and millimetres. It may be necessary, therefore, to perform a conversion to the common unit of millimetres.

2. The pipe asset database may include groups of pipes which should not be included in the analysis. Examples include privately owned lengths of main, lengths of main owned by neighbouring water companies or raw water mains. It may be desirable to eliminate these from the analysis.

7.1.2.4.1   Burst Rate by Diameter by Material

The coefficients in r_{ik} are non-dimensional and A_i is the reciprocal of time. However, to keep the answers rendered by Equation 7.8 dimensional in terms of burst rate/unit time per unit length (bursts/yr per km), it is necessary to give one of the parameters represented in r_{ik} the dimension bursts/yr per km. Burst rate as a function of diameter by material, therefore, has these dimensions. By summing lengths of mains grouped by material and diameter, and grouping burst events in the same categories, burst rates were found as shown in the relationships in Figure 7.2.

It is not the intention to discuss the details of the relationships derived in this example analysis. The interested reader is referred to Skipworth et al. (2000) where such discussion is included. The relationships derived for CI, DI and AC represent the full range of diameters that exist in the asset database. Very few bursts had been recorded in large diameter plastic (MDPE and PVC) mains. There were virtually no events in MDPE mains with diameter ≥200mm, i.e. the burst rate was effectively zero. There were too few burst events on PVC ≥200mm on which to base any meaningful analysis. Nominal burst rates would have to be attached to these material/diameter ranges.

burst rate (bursts/km per yr)

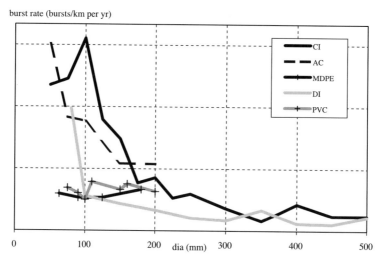

Figure 7.2: Burst rate versus diameter by material
(figures omitted from y-axis for reasons of confidentiality)

7.1.2.4.2   The Effect on Burst Rate of Density of Services

The significance of density of services scaled by pipe length was discussed in Section 7.1.2.3.

After being broken down by material and diameter, the pipe groups were broken down by density of services (scaled by mains length). As required by the burst model, the derived relationships, which would give the regression factors for inclusion in the vector r_{ik}, were non-dimensional. This means that burst rates corresponding to the homogeneous pipe groups were normalised by the average burst rate corresponding to the higher level pipe group from which they were broken down. The *effect* of density of services on burst rate was therefore isolated.

A service density was calculated for each DMA and attached to each pipe and burst corresponding to each particular DMA. Each homogeneous pipe group and burst set by material and diameter* were grouped further into service density bands and burst rate factors found as shown in Figures 7.3 and 7.4.

*Diameter Categories – It was found that there was no significant difference between different diameter categories for the same material. There were, however, two distinct categories for CI mains; up to and including 125 mm diameter and, greater than and including 150 mm diameter.

Figure 7.3 shows data points for service density categories within discrete diameter cast iron mains groups. Quantifying the scatter in Figure 7.3 is futile as the pipes and their respective failures have been broken down subjectively into service density brackets to achieve a significant portion of data in each case. This is effectively smoothing of the data, with different breakdowns resulting in different scatter.

Taking into account note* on diameter categories, Figure 7.4 shows idealised summary relationships by material between burst rate and service density. Three stage curves were observed for the metallic and MDPE mains. Two stage curves were observed for AC and PVC mains with no increase in the burst rate on PVC mains above a service density of 50 properties/km.

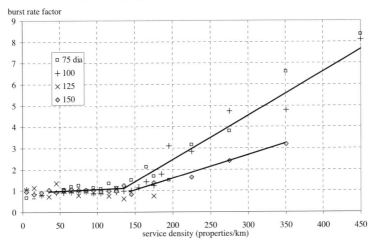

Figure 7.3: Normalised burst rate versus service density for CI mains of different diameter

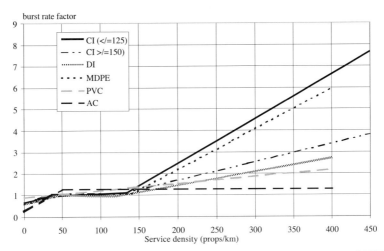

Figure 7.4: Normalised burst rate versus service density for mains of different material

7.1.2.4.3   The Effect on Burst Rate of Age

The effect of age was included in the burst model and non-dimensional coefficients had to be derived for use in r_{ik} and also for values of A_i.

As discussed in earlier sections, bursts are seldom tied to mains and this was the case in the example analysis. However, burst events can be tied to DMAs. In each DMA, the average age of each pipe category by material and diameter was calculated and this age was attached to bursts in the particular DMA corresponding to the particular material and diameter.

Pipe lengths were grouped by material and into age bands and were summed, and burst events were categorised similarly (using their implied ages) in order to find the relationships in Figures 7.5 and 7.6. Burst rates were normalised as discussed in Section 7.1.2.4.2.

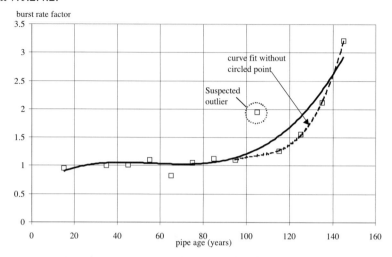

Figure 7.5: Burst rate factor versus age for CI pipes

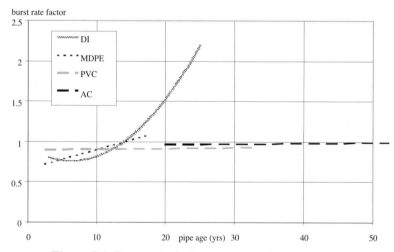

Figure 7.6: Burst rate factor versus age by material

Figure 7.5 shows the curve for CI. Two curve fits are shown, the solid one which includes the circled data point and the dashed one which shows a fit without this data point. The assumption that other variables which influence pipe failure are evenly distributed may have been particularly compromised with respect to this data point. Such an example warrants further investigation. Figure 7.6 shows curves for the other four materials considered in the analysis. The curves are, of course, limited to the age range available in the data.

7.1.2.4.4   Cumulative Methods for Deriving Burst Rate Relationships

An alternative method for finding non-dimensional burst rate factors for a given homogeneous pipe group as a function of independent variables such as diameter, service density and age is described below.

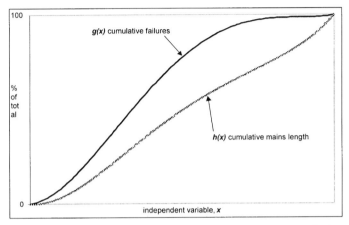

Figure 7.7: Cumulative failures as % of total failures, *g(x)*, and cumulative mains length as % of total length , *h(x)*, for a homogeneous pipe group

Database queries can be created which group failures against an independent variable (for example diameter) for a given pipe group (for example CI). Similar queries can be created for the asset database such that pipe length can be summed and grouped against the same independent variable. The information extracted via these queries can be processed to give plots of cumulative failures as a percentage of total failures against the independent variable, and cumulative length as a percentage of total length against the independent variable. Via curve fitting, these two relationships can be summarised as functions (shown as *g(x)* and *h(x)* in Figure 7.7). Non-dimensional burst rate factor plots similar to those in Figures 7.2 to 7.6 can then be found by dividing the differential of *g(x)* by the differential of *h(x)* as given in Equation 7.9.

$$b(x) = g'(x)/h'(x) \qquad\qquad (7.9)$$

where, *x* is an independent variable affecting burst rate, e.g. pipe age, diameter, service density,

     b(x) is burst rate factor as a function of *x*,

     g(x) is cumulative failures as a percentage of total failures as a function of *x*,

     h(x) is cumulative length as a percentage of total length as a function of *x*,

     g'(x) is the differential of *g(x)*,

     h'(x) is the differential of *h(x)*.

The potential advantage of this method is that it can lead directly to continuous functions and does not require the selection of appropriate bands, e.g. ranges of service density as discussed in Section 7.1.2.4.2, like those in Tables 7.1 and 7.2. However, the discrete, discontinuous nature of some of the independent variables such as diameter and age (where this has been implied and large parts of the network are assigned the same age) can make this method difficult to apply. The previous method was therefore favoured in the example analysis.

7.1.2.4.5   Distribution of Assets

There is significant interest within the UK water industry in the effect on failure rates of an ageing distribution network. Curves of the types in Figures 7.5 and 7.6 can be used at different (geographical) scales to investigate this effect. Of course, no single point can be identified on the curves as being significant at present as the point from which to progress in consideration of future years. Rather, the age of the stock of pipes is distributed through the full age range represented by the curves and across the materials. The stock of pipes is also distributed across the other variables in the analysis.

7.1.2.5   Burst Rate Allocation

It is recommended that the Methodology is applied at water supply zone (WSZ) scale. In the example analysis, there were around 2000 DMAs within 200 WSZs, i.e. WSZs are around an order of magnitude bigger than DMAs.

It is shown in this section how a burst rate is allocated to each main in an example WSZ, based on accounted for variables (Section 7.1.2.5.1) and adjustments for unaccounted for variables (Section 7.1.2.5.2), and how this is projected into the future (Section 7.1.2.5.3).

The WSZ chosen for the example application of the burst rate allocation methodology comprised 146 km of main of which 10 km was AC, 27 km was plastic, 87 km CI and 22 km DI.

7.1.2.5.1   Accounted for Variables

The attributes of length, material, diameter, age and service density are attached to each pipe in the asset database and therefore to each pipe in the chosen area. Based on this information and the relationships extracted during the company level analysis, characteristic burst rates in units of bursts/yr were attached to each pipe length within the chosen area catalogued in the asset database via Equation 7.6. This procedure lends itself easily to automation. Equation 7.6 can be modified as Equation 7.10 below for this purpose.

$$B_{ACC}(t_0) = R_{MD} F_S F_A L \qquad\qquad (7.10)$$

where, B_{ACC} (t_0) is the burst rate at time t_0 based on accounted for variables (bursts/yr),

R_{MD} is the burst rate corresponding to the pipe's material and diameter (bursts/km per yr),

F_S is the modification factor corresponding to the pipe's material and service density (dimensionless),

F_A is the modification factor corresponding to the pipe's material and age (dimensionless),

L is the mains length (km).

Allocation of these characteristic burst rates has been automated within the "Decision Tool" described in later chapters. Mathematical descriptions of curves in Figures 7.2 to 7.6 are used in order to do this. However, a separate analysis at WSZ level must be carried out in order that adjustments can be made to take account of *unaccounted for* variables at local level.

7.1.2.5.2 Unaccounted for Variables

A burst model calibration procedure is carried out in order to take account of variables not explicitly accounted for in Section 7.1.2.5.1. The steps in this calibration procedure are as follows.

1. The burst rates (in bursts/year) calculated in Section 7.1.2.5.1 are summed across the chosen area of network, grouping the bursts by material and diameter.

2. Again, grouping by material and diameter, the burst history for the chosen area is summed over the timespan of the failure database used in the analysis detailed in Section 7.1.2.4. The number of bursts corresponding to each material/diameter category is divided by the number of years to which the database corresponds resulting in burst rates in bursts/yr.

3. The burst rates generated by the model (from Step 1) and directly from the database (from Step 2) are compared. An example of such a comparison is given below.

When compared at material type level (Table 7.1), significant disagreement can be seen between the measured (directly from the failure database – Step 2) and predicted (generated by the model – Step 1) annual number of burst events. When broken down further, this disagreement is in the CI part of the network (Table 7.2 and Figure 7.8).

Table 7.1: Annual burst events by material type corresponding to example WSZ

material	bursts (/yr)	
type	measured	predicted
AC	4.4	4.1
metallic	61.8	43.0
plastic	3.4	3.3

Table 7.2: Annual burst events by diameter corresponding to CI pipes in example WSZ

CI	bursts (/yr)	
dia(mm)	measured	predicted
50	1.0	1.1
75	24.8	15.5
100	24.8	18.4
150	9.4	5.6
200	0.0	0.0
225	0.8	0.3
300	0.2	0.1
375	0.2	0.2
700	0.0	0.1
750	0.0	0.1
900	0.0	0.1
1200	0.0	0.0

4. A simple optimisation based technique to minimise the error between the calibrated model and measured burst rates yields an area and material specific adjustment factor (K_i in Equations 7.7 and 7.8). In the example shown in Figure 7.8 for the CI part of the example WSZ, K_i is 1.48. Equation 7.10 is now modified to give Equation 7.11 which takes account of unaccounted for variables. Equation

7.11 now represents the practical application of Equation 7.7 with unaccounted for variables included.

$$B(t_0) = KR_{MD}F_SF_AL \tag{7.11}$$

where, $B(t_0)$ is the burst rate at time t_0 based on accounted for and unaccounted for variables (bursts/yr),

K is the correction factor to account for unaccounted for variables for a particular pipe group.

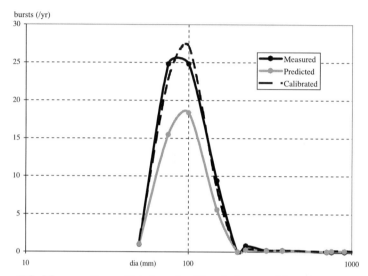

Figure 7.8: Measured, predicted and calibrated annual burst events versus diameter corresponding to CI pipes in example WSZ

7.1.2.5.3   Ageing

For illustrative purposes, Figure 7.9 below shows a schematic of a curve to describe pipe age against normalised burst rate similar to those in Figures 7.5 and 7.6. In Figure 7.9, the equation $y = f(x)$ describes the relationship between pipe age (x) and normalised burst rate (y). At current time t_0, pipe age (x) is equal to a.

Instantaneous increase in normalised burst rate

The instantaneous increase in normalised burst rate is simply the differential of $f(x)$, i.e. when $x = a$, instantaneous increase in normalised burst rate is $f'(a)$. The units of $f'(a)$ are the reciprocal of time.

Calculating the growth coefficient, A_i, for use in Equation 7.8

For an analysis period t_0 to t, where $t = t_0 + t'$, A_i can be found from Equation 7.12.

$$A_i = \frac{\ln(f(a+t')/f(a))}{t'} \tag{7.12}$$

where, A_i is the material specific growth coefficient in Equations 7.5 and 7.8,
       a is the pipe age at beginning of analysis, time t_0,
       t' is the period of analysis where $t = t_0 + t'$, and t is the time horizon (i.e. end of analysis period).

Age and material information attached to each pipe in the asset database can be used in the material specific age versus normalised burst rate relationships (e.g. Figure 7.5) within Equation 7.12 to calculate the value of the growth coefficient, A_i, for an analysis projected to the time horizon t (i.e. t' years into the future from the base year, t_0). The $e^{A_i(t-t_0)}$ part of Equation 7.8 gives the multiple by which the burst rate probability will have increased at the end of the time period t'.

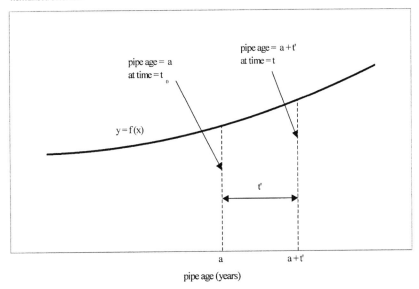

Figure 7.9: Schematic diagram of normalised burst rate versus pipe age by material

Average normalised burst rate over the period t'

Within the WLC approach to distribution network management it is necessary to calculate the total probable number of bursts over a given time period t_0 to t. The average normalised burst rate can be calculated over this period using Equation 7.13.

$$F_{aave} = \frac{\int_{a}^{a+t'} f(x) \cdot dx}{t'} \qquad (7.13)$$

where, F_{aave} is the average normalised burst rate over the period t_0 to t (i.e. t').

The total probable number of bursts, B_N, on a given pipe corresponding to the period t_0 to t, can be found by substituting F_{aave} (Equation 7.13) for F_A in Equation 7.11 and multiplying by t' to give Equation 7.14.

$$B_N = KR_{MD}F_S L \int_{a}^{a+t'} f(x) \cdot dx \qquad (7.14)$$

7.1.2.5.4   Discussion

In England and Wales, reliable failure records are only available for short historical periods, and burst events occur relatively infrequently on single pipes or in small areas of networks. For instance, in the example WSZ considered in Section 7.1.2.5, over the five year period for which burst records were taken into account, a few hundred burst events occurred in a network of several thousand pipes covering a wide range of descriptions. This is not enough on which to base any meaningful analysis, especially given the timescale over which pipe deterioration takes place and given that the large majority of pipes had suffered no failure in the period considered.

The Methodology presented provides a way of estimating failure rates on pipes across the full range of descriptions based on evidence from the surrounding area (i.e. the whole water company) collected over a relatively short time period. The Methodology then allows these estimates to be "fine tuned" to more local evidence collected over the same period. The local failure records are effectively re-distributed across the chosen network area based on explicitly accounted for variables (i.e. material, age, diameter, length and service density) and unaccounted for variables (e.g. soil conditions, network operational variables – pumping, pressure).

Where particular pipes or groups of pipes are known to have high burst rates which cannot be accounted for within the model, it may be astute to exclude them from the model and attach to them "custom" burst rates.

Once a number of burst rate allocation exercises have been carried out at WSZ level, the impact of other variables on failure rate can be studied. The accounted for variables allow an estimate of what, on average, would be expected. Adjustment factors (K_i) may then be linked to unaccounted for variables related to network operation, for example.

Find and fix policy may have varied due to the effort to control and bring down leakage levels over, say, the last five years. This is unlikely to have impacted on the distribution of mains repairs across the failure influencing variables but may have impacted on the year to year variation in and therefore the average number of mains repairs over this period. A data driven estimate of this impact may allow adjustments to be made in respect of this variable.

7.2   Customer Interruptions

Within the WLC approach to distribution network management, *Risk* is characterised in broad terms as probability multiplied by consequence. Section 7.1 dealt with the rate of structural mains failure. The consequences of a mains failure will include interruption to service for customers within a surrounding zone of influence. The subject of Section 7.2, therefore, can be considered as a sub-set of the burst model, each mains failure having attached consequences with respect to customer interruptions. These consequences must then be linked with the appropriate costs which are two-fold. Firstly, indirect costs are incurred from regulatory penalties associated with heightened levels of customer interruption through the DG3[1] serviceability measure. Secondly, external costs may be carried by customers due to

---

[1] A DG3 failure is an interruption to a customers' service of above 12 hours duration. Further, DG3 requires water companies to record and report the number of interruptions experienced by the customers that exceed 6, 12 and 24 hours.

loss of supply. In summary, as cost drivers, customer numbers and duration of interruption associated with mains failures must be quantified.

Distribution networks have inherent reliability due to their grid-like, looped layout (which is usually a function of the road layout), and the use of service reservoirs throughout networks. Many approaches to assessing the reliability of networks have been derived and a review of these and the various definitions used in reliability is given in Engelhardt et al. (2000).

In summary, three predominant approaches have been reported in the analysis of network reliability; Monte Carlo simulation, path enumeration and state enumeration. Monte Carlo simulations may be the superior technique but have an incommensurate computational cost which led to the introduction of the other two techniques. Path enumeration techniques consider the connectivity of (e.g. Goulter and Coals, 1986; Kansal et al., 1995), capacity of (e.g. Quimpo and Shamsi, 1991) or level of redundancy built into (e.g. Kessler et al., 1990) the network. State enumeration techniques differ from path enumeration techniques in that the network failure states are defined (e.g. each main is taken out of service in turn) and then checked to assess the reliability of the network in these states (e.g. Xu and Goulter, 1998; Engelhardt, 1999).

The option of using an approach based on the analysis of recent historical failure data or one based on a network hydraulic model state enumeration analysis is included in the WLC approach. These are discussed in Section 7.2.2.

7.2.1 Customer Interruption Consequences of Mains Failures

Within the regulatory framework, network reliability is covered in the DG3 serviceability measure of interruption to service of over 12 hours duration. The severity of the effects will differ between burst events in the number of customers affected. This may be a function of the description and position of the main within the network. Two extreme cases that demonstrate this are the interruptions caused by the burst of an exit main from a service reservoir and that of a small diameter dead end main.

The immediate effect of a mains burst is on the hydraulic regime within the network, compromising the pressure distribution and spatial availability of flow. To limit these effects and enable repair, valves are closed to isolate the pipe length. All customers between the shut valves will then suffer a complete loss of service. The emergency removal from service of a main may have a more extensive effect through reducing the capacity of the network to meet demands elsewhere, an extreme example being a trunk main failure. In summary, in the case of a mains failure, two failure states are relevant;

- INITIAL FAILURE STATE – the network with compromised capacity due to a large additional demand (burst flow)

- REDUCED STATE – the reduced network due to the isolation of the offending element during repair

No conclusive research is available to suggest which of the two network states should be considered in any exhaustive approach to modelling failure states. The time for which the network is in the Initial Failure State will depend on the time taken for the failure to be reported and the time taken for operatives to arrive at the site and close the valves. The time that the network will be in the Reduced State will depend on the time taken to repair the burst. Estimation of the temporal consequences (response and repair times) of mains failure may be via recorded data corresponding to these time spans.

7.2.2   Customer Interruptions within the WLC Approach

Regardless of the approach utilised, an estimate of the number of customers and the time for which their service is interrupted is required for each asset failure – this can be simplified into a customer hours quantity. Two alternative approaches have been built into the WLC framework. The first is a simplified approach whereby a customer interruption consequence (in customer hours) is attached to each failure based on a limited description of the pipe and an analysis of previous interruption data. The second approach considered is based on a more exhaustive model based analysis.

7.2.2.1   Simplified Approach

Under the DG3 serviceability measure, companies are under a regulatory obligation to record and report the loss of service experienced by their customers when mains are taken out of operation (planned or unplanned). The number of customers and the time for which they are interrupted is recorded. A DG3 failure is when the loss of a service lasts longer than 12 hours although companies must record durations of interruption greater than 6 hours, and commonly record interruptions of less than 6 hours for operational purposes.

Simple analyses have been carried out of customer interruption data corresponding to historical burst events.[2] These analyses have attempted to relate the number of customers and time of interruption to pipe diameter and DMA service density (i.e. the number of customers in the DMA scaled by the length of mains) and have revealed the following broad conclusions;

1. The average time for which a service (customer) is interrupted is insensitive to pipe diameter.
2. The average time for which a service is interrupted is insensitive to DMA service density.
3. The number of services interrupted is insensitive to DMA service density.
4. The number of services interrupted is a function of pipe diameter.

This simple analysis allows a model to be derived in the form of Equation 7.15

$$C = f(D) \qquad\qquad (7.15)$$

where, C is total customer interruption hours associated with a burst event and $f(D)$ is the number of customers affected as a function of the burst main's diameter.

Bursts on large diameter mains tend to affect a large number of customers (Conclusion 4) for the short period while remedial measures are taken to instigate a reduced but adequate network as a temporary arrangement while repair takes place. A relatively small number of customers will then tend to be affected for a relatively long time while repair takes place. In summary, interruption times are distributed across a

---

[2] These studies are unpublished as they are based on commercially sensitive data.

wide range but are concentrated in the shorter periods. The simple analyses carried out were insensitive to the small number of customers affected for a long time – these were effectively averaged out allowing Conclusion 1 to be reached. A more sophisticated analysis could be carried out such that interruption times could be differentiated, for example in order to estimate DG3 failures associated with mains failures.

Based on the limited analysis method, the repair time for a main appears to be a truly random variable (Conclusions 1 and 2). In reality, it will be related to variables such as depth of cover, ground type, surface type (e.g. whether it is metalled or not) and road classification. Although analyses could be extended to include such variables, it is doubtful whether the data would be readily available and if it were, whether the benefit from this extra complexity in the accuracy of estimate could be justified.

Conclusion 3 is perhaps the most surprising conclusion. As the density of services in an area increases a commensurate increase in the number of customers affected by a pipe failure might be expected. However, the analyses showed that this was clearly not the case. In the initial state during which the burst flow is allowed to run, in areas of lower service density where networks have largely untapped hydraulic capacity burst flows may tend to be higher and the zone of influence geographically larger. In addition, it must be considered that as the density of services increases, the number of pipe junctions and valves per unit length of main increases. With the network in its reduced state, therefore, the length of valved off main will be shorter and the number of customers on the length of temporarily redundant main will be proportionately less.

Equation 7.15 presents a simple model based on a simple analysis of historical data in order that a measure of customer interruption hours can be attached to a mains failure. Diameter is used as a proxy for the many variables which affect customer interruption numbers and duration. Although more elaborate estimates may be possible, this may suffice for the purpose of the Methodology. For the calculation of DG3 failures, an estimate can be made of the number of interruptions that will result in a DG3 failure.

7.2.2.2   *Exhaustive Hydraulic Modelling Based Approach*

An exhaustive modelling based state enumeration approach is possible within the WLC Methodology in order to observe the effect on customer interruptions of taking each main out of operation. Each main is closed in turn and a hydraulic analysis of the reduced network is carried out. Each demand node is checked against the minimum pressure requirements (or failure condition). Although the regulatory requirements imply that each consumer should be supplied with a service pressure of 15 m unless in abnormal circumstances, an estimate will be required of the pressure drop (corresponding to the DMA) which customers would notice. Where the node is identified as deficient the number of consumers affected is attributed to the interruption being simulated. This is an attempt to simulate the second phase of failure whereby the offending length of main is valved off and a reduced network is temporarily in place. However, a number of assumptions are necessary. The demand on the network at the time of failure (i.e. the time of day) must be assumed. The ability to undertake such an exhaustive analysis with any degree of realism will be dependent on the necessary information being linked to or contained within the hydraulic model. The inclusion of detail, in particular the allocation of services to demand nodes, is increasing because of the advantages associated with automating demand allocation (alternatively, nodal demands may be used to identify numbers of services).   However, in most cases establishing the distribution of services still requires assumptions.

For the majority of mains, removal from operation will only have an associated local effect. Exceptions are critical mains such as those that feed DMAs, and mains in any network with dendritic properties.   Under the conditions imposed by the reduced network, assumptions are required to define what constitutes an interruption elsewhere in the network (other than the loss of service in the valved off section of main). In addition, temporary alternative arrangements are available to the operator to minimise the wider effects. These are not accounted for in such exhaustive modelling approaches.

Clearly, as the understanding of the link between main failures and customer service is improved the implications in any assumptions made may become clearer. Further research is required to address these implications. In summary, the compound effect of the necessary assumptions associated with this exhaustive technique may render it futile. The simplified approach presented in Section 7.2.2.1 may currently be the best alternative until the assumptions associated with the state enumeration technique are addressed and the approach is made generally more robust.

CHAPTER EIGHT
Performance Based Cost Drivers III
Water Quality

8.1   Introduction

In respect of a given water quality determinant, within the Methodology an equation is used to reflect the operational cost of dealing with the risk (where actions are taken to mitigate the risk) or financial risk costs carried by the company (where no action is taken to mitigate the risk). This is not a performance model *per se* although the cost equations have a physical basis.

The three areas of water quality regulation (aesthetic, bacteriological and chemical) covered by the England and Wales Drinking Water Inspectorate (DWI) have been considered in the context of the Methodology. An "Operational Index" has now been adopted in consideration of water quality performance in Ofwat's comparative competition approach to regulation. The parameters which contribute in this index and which are influenced by the distribution network have been considered.

Within the Methodology it is considered that the distribution network does not operate in isolation. This is particularly pertinent for water quality. For example, the make up of the network determines treatment factors such as the necessary level of chlorine residual and whether phosphate dosing is necessary.

The cost of the general impact on health of water quality is borne by society through the control exercised by their agents (Ofwat, DWI). Beyond this, WLC considerations detailed herein reflect the level of risk that a company is willing to take in respect of water quality.

8.2   Background

8.2.1   Drinking Water Quality Regulation in England and Wales

The Water Supply (Water Quality) Regulations 2000 will come into full effect in January 2003, replacing the 1989 predecessor and its subsequent amendments. The new Regulations, however, include amendments to the 1989 regulations that came into immediate effect at the start of 2001. The mandatory standards of the EC Drinking Water Directive (European Commission, 1998) are found in the new Regulations, although the latter goes further in making many of the indicator parameters mandatory.

8.2.1.1   DWI's Water Quality Measures

DWI, in conjunction with WRc (Water Research Centre), have developed water quality performance indicators that have been adopted by Ofwat's comparative competition scheme. DWI Information Letter 9/99 (DWI, 1999) summarised these measures which are detailed fully in a WRc report to the DETR/DWI entitled *"Annual Compliance with Drinking Water Quality parameters – an Improved Statistical Approach"* (DETR/DWI, 2000).

The DWI concluded that two useful measures of water quality were relevant;

(a)   An OVERALL INDEX of quality of water provided by a company, calculated by averaging the mean zonal percentage compliance for 17 key parameters, giving each parameter an equal weighting, and comparing that with the average for England and Wales.

(b)   An OPERATIONAL INDEX reflecting a measure of the operational performance of treatment works and distribution networks, calculated by averaging the mean zonal percentage compliance for six parameters; iron, manganese, aluminium, turbidity, faecal coliforms and tri-halomethanes.

It is this latter OPERATIONAL INDEX, particularly in terms of the iron, turbidity, faecal coliform and tri-halomethane (THM) parameters, which is of relevance in the Methodology to distribution network management.

8.2.1.2   Section 19 Undertakings

Section 19 undertakings are associated with the duty placed on the water companies to achieve the standards set out in the Water Supply (Water Quality) Regulations 1989 and its subsequent revisions.   At the time of privatisation, the conditions of distribution networks gave rise to breaches of the compliance standards set out in the Water Supply (Water Quality) Regulations 1989. It was thus arranged that the work required to improve a network to meet the compliance standards would be undertaken by 2015. This deadline has since been brought forward to 2010. However, most undertakings will be complete by 2005.   Any future Section 19 work already scheduled must therefore be considered in investment appraisals such as the Methodology.

8.2.1.3   Operation and Maintenance Strategy

The DWI Information Note 13/98 set out the requirements for the justification of any proposed Section 19 undertakings for the price review. As a minimum, a strategic operations and maintenance (O&M) strategy was required to demonstrate that the company had met requirements under Section 19. Information Note 13/98 stated that strategies should define medium and long term strategic O&M objectives for maintaining or further improving water quality, and the means by which they would be achieved.   The O&M strategies should include procedures that prevent the deterioration of the quality of water supplied to consumers through the actions of the water company and its staff. Particular emphasis was placed on any higher level changes in the supply of the water to the consumers, i.e. changes to water treatment processes, pumping regimes and leakage management programmes.

8.2.2   Aesthetic Water Quality

Colour is dealt with in the EC Drinking Water Directive (European Commission, 1998) as an indicator parameter with the provision that it *"is acceptable to the consumers with no abnormal changes"* (as reported in Rouse, 2000). This reflects the subjectivity in the regulation of aesthetic water quality. Often, it means that a change in the aesthetic quality, even if it was under a given parametric value, will be perceived as a failure. Aesthetic water quality is dealt with in the Water Supply (Water Quality) Regulations 2000 and its predecessor through two national mandatory standards with regard to colour and turbidity. The value for colour is given on the mg/l/Pt/Co scale, with a maximum value of 20. Turbidity is measured in NTU (Nephelometric Turbidity Units) with a prescribed maximum of 4.

Discoloured water can be caused by failure at treatment or the entrainment of sediments within the network (DWI, 2000b). This entrainment usually results from hydraulic disequilibria events within the network, for example a burst or the re-valving of a zone. Sediments may originate from the corrosion of ferrous mains, the disintegration of parts of the network (for example pipe linings), through cavitation due to negative pressures which may occur due to surge, or are introduced from upstream sources. Effective and adequate treatment should eliminate this latter factor. Occasionally, however, treatment works may be ineffective in removing impurities (for example iron and manganese) which may adhere to pipe walls eventually contributing to discolouration events.

The material which leads to discoloured water at the customer's tap during or shortly after hydraulic disequilibria events is likely to originate predominantly by the corrosion of unlined ferrous mains[1] which make up a large proportion of many distribution networks in the UK. Planned mains flushing may significantly reduce or eliminate the potential for aesthetic water quality failures. Moreover, the DWI highlighted the need for water companies to develop integrated operation and maintenance strategies for all aspects of water distribution (DWI, 1998) to avoid triggering discolouration events. In summary, there is a shifting emphasis from capital to operational maintenance for the avoidance of further aesthetic water quality failures (DWI, 1998). With this in mind, it must be acknowledged that mains have a maintenance cost (and/or water quality failure liability) associated with them.

At a network level, the cost of operational maintenance to avoid aesthetic water quality failures will be closely linked to and will rise with the proportion of the network that is made up of unlined ferrous mains. It should be noted, however, that even where there are no unlined ferrous mains in a network, there may still be a cost associated with the flushing of sediments which enter the network due to inadequate treatment and from other sources. Taking this hypothesis to a further level of detail, the position of a pipe in the network must be considered. Mains which generally experience higher flow rates (and therefore sediment mobilising forces) have less potential for corrosion products and other light sediments to accumulate at their walls. However, the flow which passes through them may affect large parts of the network when compared with, say, dead end mains. The low sediment mobilising forces exerted at pipe walls in dead end mains allow sediments, including corrosion products, to remain in them increasing their potential to cause discolouration during events where unusually high flow rates (above the normal daily maximum) are passed along them. However, such discolouration events are likely to affect fewer customers.

---

[1] Many ferrous mains (cast iron, ductile iron, steel) which were originally lined have lost their linings and the definition of unlined ferrous mains, therefore, can generally be extended to include all ferrous mains.

Within the Methodology, it would be sensible to associate a cost with providing an adequate flushing programme. The extent and frequency of necessary flushing will be linked to the proportion of the network made up by unlined ferrous mains. It must be considered, however, that there may be a cost of flushing in the complete absence of unlined ferrous mains. The necessary frequency of mains flushing to keep the potential for discolouration events at an acceptable level is unknown and may be network specific due to water chemistry (AWWARF, 1996), hydraulic regime and propensity for structural failure in the particular network. However, research (e.g. Boxall et al. 2001, 2002) may go some way to answering these questions in the coming years.

In conclusion, provision must be made in the Methodology to associate an operational cost with mains flushing based on pipe material and position in the network. A cost may be associated with mains flushing in the absence of unlined ferrous mains.

NOTE

Sediments accumulate at the very ends of dead end mains where quiescent hydraulic conditions exist. These deposits necessitate periodic flushing at dead ends for their removal. However, these deposits are thought to be more onerous in their potential to harbour microbial impurities rather than their potential to contribute to water discolouration events. Accordingly, their role in distribution network water quality is considered in Section 8.2.3.2.

8.2.3   Bacteriological Water Quality

8.2.3.1   Disinfection

Where chlorination is used, a chlorine residual remains in water entering the distribution network following the disinfection process which takes place during treatment. This residual should ensure disinfection whilst the water is resident in the network. Chlorine decay occurs in the bulk of the water being transported and also at the pipe walls where microbial growth (biofilms) may be harboured. The rate of consumption of the chlorine residual will therefore depend on network make up but generally this residual will reduce with residence time or water age.

Aged, rough, generally unlined ferrous mains have a high demand for chlorine at the pipe walls and there is potentially a benefit in their replacement or relining (or mains flushing) to the level of chlorine residual required to give adequate disinfection at network extremities. It should be noted, however, that good chlorine control is a prerequisite in minimising the required chlorine residual going into the network.

High water age (i.e. long contact time with the fabric of the network) is thought to be associated with complaints of taste and odour and increased biological activity, which is why it is important to ensure a residual of free chlorine at network extremities. It follows that the higher the residence time in the network, the higher the chlorine residual required at the entrance to the network to guarantee residuals at the extremities. However, "disinfectant" taste and odour complaints are also associated with high levels of chlorine. From this point of view, therefore, it is necessary to keep the level of free chlorine at the inlet to the network to a minimum.

In summary, chlorine levels must be high enough to maintain an effective residual at network extremities, therefore avoiding bacteriological failures and taste and odour complaints associated with long contact time with the fabric of the network, but low enough to avoid disinfectant taste complaints. It is advantageous in achieving this balance, therefore, to reduce chlorine demand at the pipe walls and minimise residence time. Low contact time with the network and low demand at the pipe walls will reduce the required chlorine level at the inlet and also have the knock on effect of reducing the levels of chlorine based disinfection additives during treatment.

In summary, particularly where complaints of taste and odour are prevalent, reducing the chlorine demand of pipe walls through replacement, relining or flushing of rough mains and minimising the age of water has the potential to reduce;

- bacteriological failures,
- complaints of taste and odour associated with long contact time between the water and the fabric of the network,
- complaints of taste and odour associated with high levels of disinfectant,
- the amount of disinfection additive per unit volume of water required during treatment.

From the point of view of a Methodology, therefore, it may be advantageous to keep the maximum age of water to a minimum. There will also be benefits in the rehabilitation of mains which have a high chlorine demand and a high potential to cause bacteriological failure.

8.2.3.2   *Sediment Accumulation at Dead Ends*

Sediments accumulate at the very ends of dead end mains where quiescent hydraulic conditions exist. These deposits necessitate periodic flushing at dead ends for their removal. The division of networks into district meter areas has aggravated this problem by creating extra dead end mains.

Flushing may be carried out to remove loose accumulated deposits from the ends of dead end mains or, in the future, to remove corrosion products associated with discolouration from pipe walls. Flushing exercises in many cases, therefore, may have a dual purpose and this must be considered in the Methodology.

An operational cost should be associated with dead end mains where flushing would not otherwise be carried out.

8.2.4 Chemical Water Quality

8.2.4.1   *Iron*

The current maximum standard for iron concentration is 200 µg/l. The prevalence of cast iron mains has led to contraventions in this standard. The DWI (2000b) report noted that although there was an increase in the number of contraventions in early 1999, the latter half of the year saw a return to the general trend of significant reductions since 1996.

8.2.4.2   *PAH*

Heightened poly-aromatic hydrocarbon (PAH) levels in drinking water result from coal tar linings that are in place to reduce the internal corrosion of water mains. The current standard is 0.2 µg/l (sum of 6 individual substances) and this is to be tightened to 0.1 µg/l (reduced to sum of 4 individual substances[2]) as part of the Water Supply

---

[2] Sum of detected concentrations of benzo 3.4 fluoroanthene, benzo 11.12 fluoroanthene, benzo 1.12 perylene and indeno (1,2,3-cd) pyrene.

(Water Quality) Regulations 2000. There was a trend of increasing contravention of this standard in the early 1990s, though this receded in 1997 and a further decrease was observed in 1998 and 1999. The DWI (2000b) report indicated that the mechanics behind the release of PAHs from coal tar linings were not understood. It was speculated that the cleaning and scraping works associated with alleviating the incidence of discoloured water events increase the likelihood of contravening the PAH standard. It was noted, however, that the majority of contraventions are associated with the less harmful PAH, fluoroanthene, which is left out of the PAH parameter in the 2000 Regulations. Nevertheless, coal tar linings can still lead to failures. If coal tar lined mains are flushed or air scoured as part of rehabilitation to reduce iron or manganese then an increase in PAH is likely to occur. This must therefore be reflected in the Methodology.

8.2.4.3   THM

The THMs (tri-halomethanes) are potentially carcinogenic by-products formed when organic chemicals (such as those that occur naturally in rivers, lakes and reservoirs) are subjected to chlorination. The formation of THM compounds is minimised during the treatment process. However, it is possible for THM formation to occur in the distribution network when the residual chlorine necessary to maintain bacteriological quality, reacts with organic materials.

Dissolved organics associated with THM formation could be present in treated water due to the inability of even modern treatment works to remove them. The problem of THM formation in distribution is aggravated by the presence of rough, aged mains through two mechanisms. They tend to increase the required chlorine residual thus increasing the potential for reaction with organics in the bulk of the water and also tend to harbour biofilms which react with this chlorine and can potentially form THMs. Chlorine demand and the concentration of biological detritus in networks can be reduced by replacement or relining of old mains or by the flushing of impurities which adhere to pipe walls and are responsible for creating the high chlorine demand.

The cost of rough mains in terms of their role in elevating required chlorine levels has already been considered in Section 8.2.3.1 in consideration of bacteriological water quality. A further cost must be associated with rough mains for increasing the potential for THM formation.

8.2.4.4   Lead

High lead levels in drinking water are generally a result of the water dissolving lead as it passes through a lead service pipe. The Water Supply (Water Quality) Regulations (2000) have specified the maximum concentration of lead in drinking water as 10 µg/l. This is a substantial reduction from the existing level of 50 µg/l. The DWI (1998) report set out a timetable to meet this new standard by December 2013 with an interim level of 25 µg/l to be achieved by December 2003.

Two options, which can be used alone or in combination, exist for the reduction of lead levels in drinking water due to the existence of lead service pipes;

(a)   reducing the plumbosolvency of water at the treatment works through the dosing of phosphates and pH control,[3]

---

[3] DWI (2001) expects that pH control alone will not be sufficient to reach the 10 µg/l standard.

(b)   replacement of lead pipes.

The DWI (2000a) and DWI (2001) reports set out in more detail the requirements of the water quality regulator to ensure that the standards are met. These letters indicate how the DWI expect the water companies to meet both the interim and final standards through the two aforementioned methods.

8.2.4.5   *Other Chemicals*

The Water Supply (Water Quality) Regulations (2000) cover a large range of chemical impurities. However, other than those commented on specifically and highlighted to be impacted on in the distribution network itself, the levels of most chemical constituents do not change significantly in the distribution network. If problems exist they can usually be traced back to the treatment works and would therefore be independent of the Methodology.

8.3   Incorporation of Water Quality in a Whole Life Costing Approach to Distribution Network Management

From the background presented in Section 8.2 and its sub-sections, it is concluded that;

- Provision must be made to associate an operational cost with mains flushing based on pipe material and position in the network. A base cost may be associated with mains flushing in the absence of unlined ferrous mains.

- An operational cost is associated with dead end mains where flushing would not otherwise be carried out.

- It may be advantageous to keep the maximum age of water to a minimum.

- There is a benefit in the rehabilitation of mains which have high chlorine demand and potential to contribute to bacteriological failures.

- A cost must be associated with rough mains for increasing the potential for THM formation.

- If coal tar lined mains are disturbed as part of rehabilitation then an increase in PAH is likely to occur with accompanying taste and odour problems.

- Allowances must be made to consider the cost of treatment to reduce lead levels against the cost of lead pipe replacement, in isolation or in conjunction with rehabilitation, over the particular time horizon being considered.

In line with these summary points, water quality is now considered under the headings of Discolouration and Iron, Lead Levels, PAHs, and Disinfection and THMs.

In the distribution network, an ACTIVE or PASSIVE approach can be taken in the maintenance of water quality standards and avoidance of failures. Methods outlined in Section 8.2.1 to 8.2.4 for costing water quality considerations in the Methodology reflect the distinction shown in Figure 8.1.

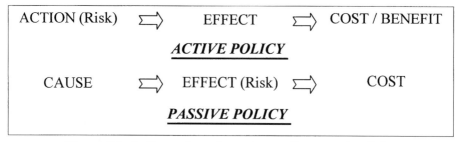

Figure 8.1: Active and passive water quality control policies

Discolouration event minimisation is predominantly by either mains replacement or flushing. These are *active* control policies. It is probable that there will be a significant move towards this latter solution (Note: the Methodology will help in selection of the best option when costed in conjunction with the full array of costs and benefits). Levels of tolerable risk of discolouration failures are decided outside the Methodology in the selected frequency of flushing. An active policy exists for lead whereby the problem of lead levels at the customer's tap can be tackled by either treatment or communication/service pipe replacement.

Risks of, for example, PAH or THM failures are unlikely to provoke any significant action in the distribution network itself although links with treated water quality are considered. However, there are "spin-off" costs and benefits in terms of the risk of failure due to rehabilitation actions. A *passive* approach is taken to THM and PAH failures whereby monetary values are assigned to the risk of failure.

The direct cost associated with any of the aforementioned failures depends on whether the incident is deemed by the regulator as trivial or not. If the failure is termed non-trivial, or likely to recur, the company could find itself prosecuted by the DWI and required to take enforced action to remedy the situation.

8.3.1 Discolouration and Iron

Two primary sources of sediment are thought to contribute in discoloured water events. Inefficient or inadequate treatment can cause sediment to be introduced into the network, depositing at dead ends and in other slack flow areas. The predominant source, however, is thought to be the build up of corrosion products at the walls of unlined ferrous mains. Changes in the flow regime within the network result in the entrainment of sediment into the flow causing discoloured water. Two approaches are available to reduce the risk of discolouration. One approach is to flush the network periodically to reduce the build up of sediment. The other is to replace unlined ferrous mains, which may, depending on the adequacy of treatment, reduce the required flushing frequency and extent of flushing. Obviously this is only relevant where unlined ferrous mains are present in the network.

At this point in time the development of an appropriate method to determine a network's required flushing frequency is being addressed by the industry and academia and as such no recommendation can be made. The spatial extent of required flushing will be dependent on the length of unlined ferrous mains and the number of dead end mains. The operational cost of flushing corresponding to a given area, therefore, could be given by Equation 8.1.

$$C_{Tflush} = \left(F \sum_{j \in AM} (v_j + w_j) L_j \right) + E_{flush} \qquad (8.1)$$

where, C_{Tflush} is the total annual cost of flushing (£),

j is a main in the network where AM is the complete set of all mains,

L_j is the length of main j,

F is the number of flushes per year which reflects the source and extent of the introduction of sediment into the network and the level of failure risk that the operator is willing to tolerate,

v_j is the annual cost associated with the particular main based on whether the main is thought to be a source of sediment build up (£/unit length per year),

w_j is the annual cost associated with the particular main based on whether the main is thought to be a source of discolouration through corrosion (£/unit length per year). And w_j would equal 0 if the main is not an unlined ferrous main,

E_{flush} is the sum of annual externalities associated with flushing (£/year).

Although not always the case, iron contraventions often occur as a result of discoloured water events. Equation 8.1 does not directly deal with the risk of iron contraventions. It is thus necessary to distinguish the risks associated with contravening the iron standard from the risk of discoloured water events. The risk cost associated with contravening the iron standard is given by Equation 8.2.

$$C_{FE} = \left(R_{FE} \sum_{i \in UF} x_i L_i \right) + E_{FE} \qquad (8.2)$$

where, C_{FE} is the annual cost associated with the risk of iron contravention (£/year),

R_{FE} is the annual risk cost associated with a unit length of unlined ferrous main (£/unit length per year),

i is an unlined ferrous main in the network where UF is the complete set of all unlined ferrous mains,

L_i is the length of each main i,

x_i is a weighting factor for each main (dimensionless). Note that x_i reflects the likelihood of the release of iron into solution or suspension in the particular main.

E_{FE} is the sum of annual externalities associated with contravening the iron standard (£/year).

Equations 8.1 and 8.2 best demonstrate the difficulty of addressing water quality within the Methodology. Flushing itself will imply that the build up of iron sediments is removed. This implies that the risk or the contravention of the iron standard is reduced. This may not necessarily be the case, as flushing may expose the mains to further corrosion, or the flushing itself may increase the iron content above the standard. This though can be easily reflected in the choice in the value of R_{FE}, which may change depending on F.

8.3.2 Lead

Two approaches can be taken where lead concentrations at the customer's tap exceed permitted levels. It is possible to add phosphates during treatment to lower the plumbosolvency of the treated water. Alternatively, a service pipe replacement programme can be undertaken. The possibility exists of replacing these lead pipes opportunistically in conjunction with mains replacement.

A provision for the entry of a phosphate cost is included in the Methodology as coded in ExSoft. However, no service pipe replacement model is included.

8.3.3 PAH

Where coal tar linings exist, the risk of their disturbance and concomitant PAH contraventions also exists. A cost must be associated with this risk. It is suggested that Equation 8.3 is used to describe the annual cost associated by the water company with the risk of PAH failure in a given network.

$$C_{PAH} = R_{PAH} L_{CT} + E_{PAH} \qquad (8.3)$$

where, C_{PAH} is the annual cost associated with the risk of PAH contravention (£/year),

R_{PAH} is the risk cost associated with a unit length of coal tar lined main (£/unit length per year),

L_{CT} is the length of coal tar lined mains,

E_{PAH} is the sum of annual externalities associated with contravening the PAH standard (£/year).

8.3.4 Disinfection and THMs

Disinfection in the network presents a twofold problem. If disinfection residuals are too low, there is a risk of bacteriological failure and taste and odour complaints (stale water). On the other hand, if chlorine residuals are too high there is a risk of THM formation and taste and odour complaints (disinfectant). In summary, the risks carried by the operator are incurring taste and odour complaints, incurring bacteriological failures and elevating THM levels which cause contravention.[4]

There is a benefit in lowering the chlorine demand of the network by replacing mains which create a high demand for chlorine. However, water companies in England and Wales tend to operate integrated systems of treatment works and distribution networks. In theory, the required chlorine residual in the water leaving the works must be such that an adequate residual is present at all extremities of the distribution networks it may have to serve. Because of the integrated nature of systems, changing mains in a given network is unlikely to impact on the residual required at the treatment works. The possibility of lowering the identified costs through lowering chlorine levels is therefore discounted.

However, it must be considered that aged, hydraulically rough mains increase the risk of bacteriological and THM failures. The degree by which this risk is increased is

---

[4] In line with DWI (1999) which stated that there is no evidence linking THMs with cancer and so any costs associated with such a link, if it exists, are ignored.

dependent on the likely presence of tuberculation. It is suggested that Equations 8.4 and 8.5 below are used to describe the annual cost associated by the water company with the risk of THM and bacteriological failures in a given network.

$$C_{THM} = \left(R_{THM} \sum_{i \in UF} y_i L_i \right) + E_{THM} \tag{8.4}$$

where, C_{THM} is the annual cost associated with the risk of THM contravention (£/year),

i is an unlined ferrous main in the network where UF is the complete set of all unlined ferrous mains,

R_{THM} is the risk cost associated with a unit length of unlined ferrous main (£/unit length per year),

y_i is a weighting factor for each main (dimensionless). And y_i reflects the likelihood that the particular main will contribute to a THM contravention

E_{THM} is the sum of annual externalities associated with contravening the THM standard (£/year).

$$C_{BAC} = \left(R_{BAC} \sum_{i \in UF} z_i L_i \right) + E_{BAC} \tag{8.5}$$

where, C_{BAC} is the annual cost associated with the risk of bacteriological contravention (£),

i is an unlined ferrous main in the network where UF is the complete set of all unlined ferrous mains,

R_{BAC} is the risk cost associated with a unit length of unlined ferrous main (£/unit length),

z_i is a weighting factor for each main (dimensionless), where z_i reflects the likelihood that the particular main will contribute to a bacteriological contravention

E_{BAC} is the sum of annual externalities associated with contravening the bacteriological standards (£/year).

Where UV or ozonation methods of disinfection are used, y_i will always be equal to zero and z_i must be adjusted to take account of the change in the risk of bacteriological failure.

8.3.5 Discussion

The values of the R in Equations 8.2 to 8.5 represent the risks that the water company takes on as the owner and operator of the network. The R terms reflect the potential costs (divided by the unlined ferrous mains length) such as fines, increased administrative burden, e.g. legal costs.

The values of x_i, y_i and z_i are non-dimensional factors which reflect the risk of iron, THM and bacteriological failures introduced predominantly by different degrees of tuberculation. Indicators for this presence may be hydraulic roughness coefficients taken from hydraulic network models. However, such roughness values may be inaccurate especially where mains are hydraulically independent. In the absence of reliable model data to describe the roughness of unlined ferrous mains, other sources of information may be sought. However, in the light of current knowledge it may be that unit constants are applied.

Equation 8.3, in respect of PAH failures, has a slightly different form from Equations 8.2, 8.4 and 8.5. Weighting factors for each main in Equation 8.3 are not included. In this form of equation, the whole length of coal tar lined main (L_{CT}) is assumed to carry an equal risk. This is equivalent to the weighting factors being all equal to 1. For simplicity, and in the light of current knowledge, Equations 8.2, 8.4 and 8.5 could be modified and given this form.

CHAPTER NINE
Decision Support and Integration of WLC Components

9.1   Introduction

Chapter 9 introduces and discusses the final element of the Methodology, the "Decision Tool". The "Decision Tool", as represented within Figure 1.3, integrates the models contained within the "WLC Accounting" and "Network Performance" modules onto a single platform, establishing the links between the costs and the quantities that drive them. Thereon it allows each such link to be investigated and tracked, assessing the implications of each activity in terms of performance and consequential cost.

Knowledge built through establishing and investigating these links, influences decisions relating to water distribution networks. Therefore, the "Decision Tool" represents the primary source of decision support supplied by the Methodology. The support supplied a decision making process can be provided in a variety of forms and at various levels of detail. This ranges from simple guidance through to legal specifications. WLC has been utilised as decision support across this spectrum, although it is yet to be included as legal specification. The nearest to this is in the USA where LCC (life cycle costing) analysis is required for all roadwork projects that utilise government funding (Arditi and Messiha, 1999).

At is simplest, WLC supplies a decision-maker a set of cost streams, each representing an alternative through which one can develop an understanding. Each cost stream reflects a set of input costs and modelled relationships. To provide decision support, the resultant cost streams require a context that will enable them to be assessed and/or ranked. This context may originate externally, with WLC representing the economic assessment in a much larger decision framework. Equally, WLC alone provides a context through which decisions can be made. An example of this is to determine the strategy that has the least whole life cost.

Decision support also varies in the degree of optimisation provided. At its fundamental level, optimisation is the determination of the "best" alternative. Information supplied to a decision maker comes at different levels of detail. For example, WLC supplies cost streams that can inform a purely subjective-based decision making process. These cost streams could be used by the decision maker to prioritise the different alternatives, effectively identifying the "best" alternative. Provision of a further level of detail within the decision support can be achieved by applying automated search techniques. These techniques utilise computers for their brute simulation power, identifying the "best" from a large number of alternatives that would otherwise be unfeasible. Caution must be exercised in the use of these techniques, but equally it must be recognised that through computer aided algorithms, problems can be optimised to a degree that cannot be achieved through a trial and error exercise.

Due to the variation in the decision support that can be supplied by WLC, this chapter addresses what can be supplied rather than being prescriptive. To provide guidance on how this decision support manifests itself, a review of the models that have appeared in past literature and those that are presently available is supplied.

An important step in determining the appropriate level and form of the decision support, is the identification of limiting factors. Constraints may originate from knowledge and understanding in the scientific community, IT issues, and the prejudices of the decision-maker. In Chapters 6 through 8 this book has already addressed the limitations in the scientific community with respect to water distribution networks. To address the second issue, Section 9.2 in part presents a discussion on the implications of what has to date been presented in the various sub-modules of the "WLC Accounting" and "Network Performance" modules. Greater consideration is given to the implications with respect to the IT requirements in Chapter 10. This chapter finishes with discussion on the decision support that can be provided by the Methodology.

9.2   Requirements placed by the "WLC Accounting" and "Network Definition" Sub-modules

The primary role of the decision tool is to provide a platform through which the links between the cost entries within the "WLC Accounting" and the values as modelled within the "Network Definition" module can be established. Implicit in this statement is that this single platform must meet the requirements placed by the constituent sub-modules. Section 9.2.1 and Section 9.2.2 discuss the implications of what has preceded in this book for the "WLC Accounting" and "Network Definition" modules.

9.2.1   WLC Accounting Module

Chapter 5 detailed the development of the cost entries for application in the regulatory framework in England and Wales. The format of the output from the "WLC Accounting" identifies amongst others, the links between the variable costs and their drivers. Without doubt, the limitation of the format of these cost entries will come from the costs that are stored within a company. Therefore, the "Decision Tool" will need to reflect the information being passed to it, thus providing the decision-maker with the support as required by the "WLC Accounting". For example, throughout this book the ability to incorporate social costs into the Methodology has been highlighted. Their inclusion was made within the "WLC Accounting" module. Continuing this distinction through the "Decision Tool" will enable the decision-maker to differentiate and thus investigate the impact of the decision. Without this distinction this will be not be possible.

In this way, it is difficult to be prescriptive in highlighting what is necessary when determining what features of the accounting scheme should be brought through and encapsulated into the "Decision Tool". It will be determined by the requirements of each application and modeller. However, a number of possibilities in representing the costs within a "Decision Tool" include;

• allow all costs to be tracked throughout the period of analysis,

- make a distinction between the private and social costs,

- allow for the costing to be associated into larger categories, for example, RAG 4.01 associates all costs to either "Normal Operation", "Bursts" or "Leakage",

- establish and represent the links between the variable costs and their cost drivers for all cost entries,

- provide functionality to observe effects on discount rate and period of analysis.

9.2.2 Network Definition

A prerequisite of integrating "Network Performance" onto a single platform is to provide functionality required to quantify all the cost drivers. Considering the elements given in Chapters 6 through 8, the "Decision Tool" should be able to, for any given action identified as an intervention,

- characterise the assets that make up the network within the area to be defined to allow the relationships defined in the performance sub-modules to be populated,

- update the asset inventory over the period of analysis,

- make the necessary links to appropriate computer simulation models (e.g. hydraulic models) to assess the performance of the intervened network,

- update the quantities that drive costs over the period of analysis.

Although Chapters 6 through 8 provide the holistic performance framework, not all the cost drivers are covered therein. These chapters concentrated on modelling the delivery of appropriate service to the customers, whereas the cost drivers identified within the "WLC Accounting" module also include the assets within the network. For example, many of the costs identified in the example provided in Chapter 10 are linked to the number of customers. This may or may not vary over time. If it is the former, it will need to be accounted for in the "Decision Tool".

9.3   Historical Look at Decision Support

Traditionally, there has been a reliance on engineering judgement in determining required levels of expenditure and courses of action for water distribution networks. However, there has been an increasing recognition that these decisions require larger degrees of decision support to meet the increased need for justification and auditability. This movement from engineering judgement to decision support tools has been mirrored by the various models introduced in both the academic and industrial literature over the past 30 years. Where possible comment has been made on the models currently available in the industry, although this is limited by the material that is publicly available.

When presenting this review, the terminology utilised is different to that in the rest of this book. Reference is continually made to the term *rehabilitation*. This general term for maintenance events encapsulates the activities referred to as "Operational Interventions" and "Pipe Interventions", although most commonly the latter. Terminology differences are most apparent in respect of the performance modelling. For the purposes of this review, the performance criteria are denoted here by the terms *economic, hydraulic, reliability, water quality* and *operational*. The terms used here are in line with a more comprehensive review of the field undertaken by Engelhardt et al. (2000).

A clear distinction has been made in presenting the various decision models on the level of decision support provided. The first two model types, general rehabilitation guides and prioritisation models provide details on the suitability of assets to undergo rehabilitation. Often these models provide a ranking system. A decision is subsequently required to identify which actions will or will not be required. The final set of decision models differs in that these decisions themselves are made. This process is automated utilising a search or optimisation technique.

9.3.1   General Guides

Early attempts at providing decision support for water distribution networks investigated decisions for each main (or asset) in isolation. There was no attempt made within these models to prioritise the rehabilitation requirements. Furthermore, it was common for assessment to be centred around a single performance measure, with the final decision tempered by the implicit consideration of the other performance measures.

Shamir and Howard (1979) used a net present value analysis of the future burst costs and the cost of replacing the main to decide whether replacement would be economically beneficial. In the same vein, Walski and Pelliccia (1982) defined a critical break rate which, if exceeded, would indicate that the main should be replaced. Walski (1982) guided the relining decision through consideration of the associated cost savings in pumping and energy. Walski (1985) extended this concept by providing an equation to identify the length of main that needed to be lined, or if necessary, whether a parallel main was required.

9.3.2   Prioritisation Models

In addition to the functions of the general guides discussed above, prioritisation models attempt to rank the mains requiring rehabilitation such that for a given budget, the actions with the most benefit can be identified. Since the determination of the budget is exogenous to the decision making process, the performance of the final rehabilitated system in terms of hydraulics, reliability or water quality is not considered.

9.3.2.1   Models for Prioritising Component Rehabilitation

In common with the general rehabilitation models discussed in Section 9.3.1, the prioritisation models often concentrated on the consideration of a single performance measure. For example, Quimpo and Shamsi (1991) used a minimum cut set reliability approach to place an importance factor on each main. A minimum cut set is defined as the smallest set of pipes that cause the system to fail. In this case, failure is defined as the loss of connectivity of the supply to one of the demand nodes. Like Quimpo and Shamsi (1991), Schneiter et al. (1996) used a capacity based reliability approach which gave priority to those mains which would provide the most improvement in the system wide capacity reliability. Schneiter et al. (1996) applied this prioritisation model to a simplified network and acknowledged that the required computing time would prohibit its use on a large network. To prioritise mains rehabilitation, the approach developed in Waterfowl by WRc (Anon. (1997a)) utilised a whole life costing approach to prioritise both the time and method of rehabilitation for each component. The approach encompassed by UTILNETS (Anon. (1997b)) assigned a reliability index to each main based on hydraulic and structural reliability and the effect of the main on water quality.

9.3.2.2   *Prioritising System Wide Rehabilitation Decisions*

Kane (1994) used a prioritisation approach to allocate funds by district. A subjective point scoring system was utilised which was based on the failures that had occurred in the system in the previous year. As this decision model was developed for a system in the UK, the failures were primarily defined by the levels of service measures proposed by Ofwat. Although not strictly a prioritisation model, Deb et al. (1998) provided software (KANEW) that made system wide renewal rate decisions for different main categories. The model utilised the cohort survival model (Herz, 1996) to provide both an upper and lower limit to the required renewal rate. The output from this model compared favourably against the renewal rates of four water companies in the USA.

9.3.2.3   *Criticality Models*

A number of authors have presented what are termed *criticality models* (PPK, 1993; Anderson et al., 1997; Louws, 1997; Vincent et al., 1997). These models are essentially prioritisation models, utilising the basic decision framework illustrated in Figure 9.1. The decision to replace and the urgency of replacement is based on the condition of the main, or more precisely the risk of it failing, and its criticality as a component to the distribution network. This conceptual decision framework can also be visualised in terms of the equation below.

$$\text{Loss Potential} = \text{Risk} \times \text{Consequences}$$

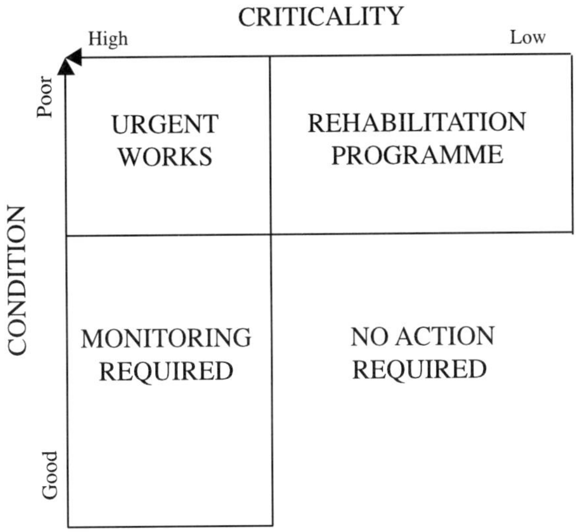

Figure 9.1: Criticality Based Approach

9.3.3   Optimisation Models

Optimisation techniques consider the interaction of each main with the system as a whole. They allow for both the performance and cost of the rehabilitated system to play a role in the formulation of the rehabilitation programme. The approaches which have been reported include the optimisation of performance given a cost constraint (Li and Haimes, 1992b) and the minimisation of cost given a performance constraint

(Walski, 1987a; Lansey et al., 1992; Kim and Mays, 1994; de Schaetzen et al., 1998; Kleiner et al., 1998). These optimisation techniques can also be used to consider network rehabilitation as a multi-objective problem (Halhal et al., 1997; Engelhardt, 1999). This approach allows for the trade-off between the system performance and the cost of rehabilitation.

Optimisation techniques require large numbers of trial evaluations to obtain near global optimal solutions. To create a practical formulation in terms of computational requirements, therefore, many of the models to date only consider one or two performance measures. Where there is more than one, simplified models or measures are utilised.

9.3.3.1   *Optimising the Availability of a Rehabilitated System*

Li and Haimes (1992b) provided an optimisation technique that utilised the system availability as the objective function and utilised the Markov model developed by Li and Haimes (1992a). They modelled the states of deterioration of a main, following the probabilistic model of Andreou et al. (1987), and included the state of planned rehabilitation. Therefore, the decision of whether to replace or repair could be made to maximise the probability that the main was operational at any time in its deterioration. Li and Haimes (1992b) applied this Markov based deterioration model on a simplified network, maximising the system availability given a cost constraint. As with the earlier reliability work of Beim and Hobbs (1988), a Markov based model required large computational times, which was reflected in the application of the proposed model to a simplified network.

9.3.3.2   *Optimising the Economics of a Rehabilitated System*

Lansey et al. (1992) minimised rehabilitation cost subject to a hydraulic performance constraint. Two time steps were considered, such that works were scheduled for the current time and 10 years hence given that there would be an increase in the demand on the system. De Schaetzen et al. (1998) used a similar approach restricted to a single time step. Instead of minimising the rehabilitation cost, Kim and Mays (1994) and Engelhardt (1999) used slightly different approaches and minimised the operating cost, to include rehabilitation, pumping and maintenance costs. Engelhardt (1999) extended this approach by allowing the replacements to be scheduled over a 20 year period. The 20 year period was split into four, five-year time periods. The model allowed for mains replacements to be scheduled in any of these time intervals, with the expenditure in each period constrained by the available funds. Kleiner et al. (1998) used an extended planning horizon to identify the time to the next rehabilitation and a cycle time between replacements for each main in the network. The time to first replacement was a function of the structural deterioration through corrosion and the increase in hydraulic roughness. The time between future replacements was purely a function of structural deterioration. The structural deterioration was considered as part of an economic analysis of future maintenance costs and, as in earlier models, (Shamir and Howard, 1979; Walski and Pelliccia, 1982) provided an optimum time of replacement.

9.3.4   Comments

The models throughout the literature provide decision support, ranging from providing guidance within a larger framework, to making the decision themselves through automating the process. Observing the models as presented implies that there exists a direct link between the level of decision support and the degree of optimisation. For example, the guides as presented in Section 9.3.1 provide no means of optimisation, yet as is suggested, are only part of a much larger decision. The prioritisation models rank the various alternatives, optimisation is achieved by choosing the best given some measure in relative terms. The optimisation models detailed in Section 9.3.3, referred to more recently as "formal optimisation" techniques (UKWIR, 2002) provide the "best" alternative in absolute terms. Such models need these absolute measures to be automated, thus more information that must accurately be identified. Clearly, there exists a link between the information and effort required and the level of decision support that is being aimed for. It should be reiterated, these models supply support rather than take decisions.

The models also introduce another important factor in considering water distribution networks in terms of decision support. Decisions that effect network performance can be taken at a number of hierarchical levels. The majority of the models presented in the review concentrate on considering individual pipe elements in isolation. Others account for the fact that these individual components make up a much larger system. A few considered making decisions at the network level (Kane, 1994), removing the consideration of pipes as individual elements. The pipes in this case were bundled together as a set of assets.

The granularity of the assets in the decision making process will depend on the hierarchical level at which the decision is made. Across a wide geographical area, the consideration of pipes to an elemental level is computationally unfeasible. Whereas, within well constrained geographical boundaries, decisions can be made down to the elemental level.

9.4   Decision Support supplied by WLC

WLC can supply decision support at various levels in terms of "hierarchical" and "optimisation" levels. It can act as a rehabilitation guide or a prioritisation model, providing a single monetary value for a set of actions, or scenario. Various scenarios could be run, allowing ranking in terms of this monetary value. In many cases, for example when considering options within a sustainability context, this may be all that is required from WLC. When considering social and environmental benefits it may be deemed inappropriate or too difficult or expensive to value these as costs. In which case, WLC is the economic component in a larger decision framework.

Within this context, the WLC of a scenario would represent one more attribute that can be used to assess it against the set of available alternatives. On the other hand, WLC itself can provide the context, or the objective for a decision making framework. An example of this is to minimise the WLC. Once WLC has been placed within a defined context or objective, the automation of the scenario investigations becomes an alternative. This allows the decisions within the particular scenario to "best" meet the defined objective to be identified explicitly. This automation is readily achieved through the use of search techniques, such as the genetic algorithm (Goldberg, 1989).

When automating such decisions, the preferences and requirements of the decision-maker's role within an organisation would need to be explicitly given. For example, in determining the required levels of expenditure an individual would attempt to minimise the whole life costs over the period of analysis, whilst constraining performance. Another individual within the organisation will be responsible for determining how to maximise the benefits of this defined expenditure. These two definitions differ, with the differences borne out in the objective utilised within the automated decision making routine.

It is the role of the "Decision Tool" to meet the decision support requirements being placed on the Methodology. These requirements will determine the level of decision support, the context that WLC is being placed within the decision making framework, and the hierarchical level of application. It has to be noted that the decision support supplied by the Methodology is not entirely encompassed within the "Decision Tool". The steps in developing the models and cost accounts detailed throughout the Methodology provide decision support. This may be in terms of identifying where knowledge is deficient, if necessary providing guidance on where resources should be allocated to improve the knowledge available to the organisation.

As an example, consider the "WLC Accounting" module. This module requires the cost data within an organisation to be analysed and directly attributed to the activities (or quantities) that drive them. Initially, the ability to do this will be dependent on how the costs are recorded and stored. The task of breaking down these costs, may identify areas where costs are much higher than they ought to be, or areas where efficiencies could be gained. It may also suggest better ways in which the costs should be recorded to ensure that the costs could be linked with their drivers. This is by no means an exhaustive list, however it does indicate how decisions within an organisation can be influenced.

CHAPTER TEN
Integration of WLC Components and Decision Support

10.1   Introduction

An important element in any WLC application is the assimilation of the input data onto a single platform in a manner that enhances the decision making process. Similar to having no information, excess information with little associated context hinders rather than clarifies the decision making process. This chapter investigates the data flow and the connections that will need to be created between the "Decision Tool" and the often disparate external databases that store the performance data and the cost information. Mapping the flow of data from their storage systems, through the individual modules and on through the "Decision Tool" element is an indispensable step to ensure that extraneous data is not collected, analysed and thus presented to the decision maker.

The WLC software must also meet the requirements placed on the support that it is intended to supply to a decision making process. On a more micro-level the software needs to reflect the various elements as identified in the "WLC Accounting" and implied into the "Network Definition" sub-modules. The nature of these modules and water distribution systems in general, implies that generic WLC software can become complex.   Therefore, to add value to the discussion presented, the generic requirements placed by the modular "WLC Accounting" and "Network Performance" are identified. Alongside of this, a discussion is given into the example software that was developed in parallel with the Methodology.

There are a number of key points to remember in what is presented in this chapter. The Methodology as presented within this book is nascent with no off-the-shelf software existing. It is not envisaged, given the differing nature of water industries, computer facilities and software platforms that the software example presented throughout is the panacea. As such, it is appreciated that custom solutions will need to be derived based on the generic implementation but possibly to include further complexities (or simplifications) and tailored to existing corporate software setups.

10.2   WLC Decision Support

Decisions that affect performance, ultimately accruing as costs, can be made at various operational hierarchical levels and by different individuals within an organisation. The "Decision Tool" will need to reflect this. The Methodology has been developed around determining the required expenditure levels throughout the period of analysis. As such, ExSoft has been developed to support determining the least whole life cost operational and maintenance strategy for the water distribution network. This decision support has been developed around a two stage process.

The first stage of decision support could be referred to as the calculation of the WLC. By assimilating the data for the "WLC Accounting" module with the "Network Performance" sub-modules, it provides the user with the ability to investigate different investment and operational decisions. In line with the defined scenario a set of accounts is generated. Another scenario can then be run, and the cost accounts compared. This provides the decision maker with the ability to observe the inter-relationships between the various modules.

To support the decision maker, ExSoft provides the decision-maker with the ability to,

- calculate the whole life cost for any scenario,

- observe each cost driver and cost over the period of analysis, allowing the cost observed to be linked directly to the performance/attribute that is driving it,

- develop a set of accounts for each time period or a summary of the costs over the period of analysis,

- observe various user-defined scenarios (whether operational, risk or costing) quickly,

- allow the investigation of the sensitivity of the various input parameters on the WLC,

- allow the change in operation and maintenance of the infrastructure assets over the period of analysis.

The second level of decision support utilises an automated search technique to find the best alternative out of the complete set of available options for the defined scenario. It is envisage that this second level of decision support should only be undertaken as a final step. A firm understanding of the values being placed into the search is required as any uncertainty and lack of confidence in the input data will be carried through.

10.3   Representation of a Water Distribution Network within a WLC Analysis

The representation utilised for a water distribution network within WLC software should reflect the operational hierarchy of the supervising company/authority. It should allow the operational and investment decisions to be considered at the appropriate level. For example, decisions that contribute to leakage management (e.g. pressure reduction) are made at a network level. Decisions that focus on the pipe infrastructure can be grouped at various levels of granularity. ExSoft represents the pipe infrastructure in three levels of granularity. One of these is to classify pipes within the network in terms of material and diameter, referred to here as pipe classes. Therefore, when a decision is made, it is for all pipes represented by this pipe class, regardless of location or connectivity. The lowest granularity considered is to use the definition of pipes as represented in an all mains hydraulic model.

Where possible, water distribution networks rely on gravity fed supplies. Requirements are placed on these systems by operating pressure head constraints. These two factors have resulted in the creation of distinct areas within networks, generally defined by the topography of the area. Due to the statutory requirements placed on controlling leakage in the UK, the networks are given greater granularity through the setting up of distinct isolated sub-networks (or DMAs) to provide greater pressure management. As with other places in the world, this has led to the establishment of a well-defined hierarchical structure for water distribution networks in England and Wales. Regardless of the hierarchical structure utilised in operating a water distribution network, each area needs to be characterised in terms of the;

- cost drivers identified with the "WLC Accounting",

- costs identified in the "WLC Accounting",

- activities and interventions that may occur within the area,

- pipe assets that make up the network, such that the relationships defined in the performance sub-modules can be populated.

There exist implications for applying the Methodology and representing water distribution networks at different hierarchical levels within an organisation. It is difficult to list these whilst providing the necessary context to explain them in a generic manner. Rather this is left to later, when ExSoft and the results generated are discussed in Chapter 11.

10.4   Handling WLC Data

In assimilating the required data onto a single platform, connections will be required to be made with databases possibly distributed throughout the company. Figure 10.1 provides a conceptual representation of the connections that may be necessary and how the data flows through the Methodology. Clearly, there are three distinct sections of Figure 10.1. The first of these is the external sources of the data used in the WLC decision support. The second represents the first stage of the decision support, the single platform that allows the assimilation of the WLC data. The third section is associated with the automation of the decision making process, or the second step in the decision making process.

For most water companies, the centerpiece of the infrastructural asset registers is a GIS package. This platform stores the physical data of these assets, and possibly performance data. The data stored on this platform is required throughout the Methodology at a number of levels. For example, hydraulic models are increasingly constructed from GIS databases. If the network definition module requires the explicit inclusion of the hydraulic model, the majority of pipe asset information can be imported through this connection. Note, that there is a convergence occurring within the software being supplied to the industry. Increasingly hydraulic modelling packages supply GIS capabilities, whilst GIS packages developed for the water sector supply hydraulic model capabilities. The various performance models detailed in the "Network Performance" module are rational data derived relationships. Ultimately, the data that is utilised to derive these relationships will be recorded in a database. Figure 10.1 identifies that the system in question could be the GIS, although this will obviously not always be true.

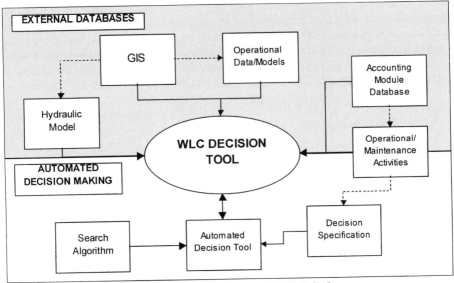

Figure 10.1: Possible Layout of WLC Software

The flow of data from the GIS package into the WLC Software is difficult to define. Data that may flow through this link may include;

- data that characterises the network that has been identified as a driver (i.e. the population, customers and consumers served),

- the pipe network characteristics in the event that no hydraulic model is included within the analysis,

- performance data (i.e. results from a leakage assessment and burst records),

- cost data (this is increasingly being recorded on GIS),

- operational and maintenance activities undertaken on the network.

The "WLC Accounting" module as detailed relies on an activity based approach. Although it has been identified that costing information is increasingly finding its way onto GIS, it is doubtful that it will be stored in a format that is readily inputted. Therefore, it is likely that the WLC software will need to make a connection to another external database that has consolidated the cost information.[1]

In all connections with external databases it is important that it is identified early where the links are bi-directional. Data will be updated, changed and added to throughout the application of the Methodology. If it has been identified that these changes and additions to data need to be captured and not lost, an appropriate feedback loop will need to be established. Beyond identifying this as an issue, it is difficult to make further comments on this due to the large number of data handling protocols and permissions generally put in place by an organisation to protect the integrity of the data stored on their corporate systems.

---

[1] Cost data for various activities within an organisation are often held in disparate databases themselves.

An overarching issue of the "WLC Accounting" and "Network Definition" modules is the identification of the various management activities (i.e. interventions) available. Once identified, these activities need to be costed and the effect of each activity on the set of cost drivers must be incorporated and accounted for. This information needs to be inputted and will be required to be accessed by two sections of Figure 10.1 that represent the software's decision support elements. Whereas, for all other elements of Figure 10.1 the data flow passes through the first level of decision support to the automation process, interventions are an exception as they represent decision variables. More details on decision variables within the "Automated Decision Tool" are in Chapter 12.

The bottom section of Figure 10.1 represents the second level of the decision making support that could be offered. Two distinct elements are identified here that feed into the automated decision tool, the search technique utilised and a decision specification box. The latter of these provide the functionality to define the formulation and the decisions that are required of the automated decision tool. The bi-directional link between the two levels of the decision tool should be highlighted as this will allow post-optimisation sensitivity analysis of the identified solution.

10.5   PILOT Software

The PILOT software developed in parallel to the WLC methodology provides a solution to the issues that have been presented in this chapter. It is not presented as the panacea, though this should not lower the value in presenting the software, as it can easily be adapted for real world uses.

10.5.1 The Layout and Form of the PILOT Software

To meet the requirements placed on the development of PILOT Software for the England and Wales regulatory requirements, the data available, the connections required to external databases and search techniques, it was decided to develop stand alone software. ExSoft was written in C++ with the basic layout provided in Figure 10.2, and follows closely Figure 10.1. The top two elements (in dashed boxes) represent the external databases that store the data that is required to be brought into the process. The differentiation between these two elements is based on the platform that stores the input data. The element below these two represents the main interface of the "Decision Tool", whilst the remaining elements relate to the automated decision-making element. More details of each of these elements is provided below.

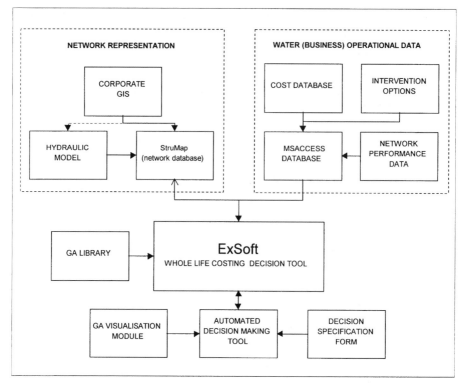

Figure 10.2: The overall software layout

1. Network Representation

This element encapsulates the necessary information on pipe attributes and, where it is deemed necessary for the analysis, the hydraulic model. The pilot software is linked with StruMap (Geodesys ©) through its associated programmers interface (API). StruMap provides the functionality of a GIS but has been linked with numerous operational tools including a hydraulic modelling package (HARP). The pipe data is imported through the established connection, and assigned to each water system area.

2. Water (Business) Operational Data

This element represents the other data and physical relationships required by the Methodology. Within ExSoft, this information is consolidated and imported through a MSAccess database. The information that is brought in here includes;

- the output of the WLC Accounting module (including any targets),
- the interventions that can be undertaken within the areas,
- details of the pipe materials,
- burst, roughness relationships.

3. GA Library

The genetic algorithm (GA) library incorporated into the software is that utilised in the majority of the work undertaken at the Centre for Water Systems (de

Schaetzen et al., 1998). The library is a collection of object oriented classes that can readily be controlled by the user.

4. *Whole Life Costing Decision Tool*

This element encapsulates the first level of the WLC decision support. It consists of a single form that allows the user to investigate each of the performance models and the cost entries of the "WLC Accounting" module.

5. *Automated Decision Making Tool*

This element encapsulates the interface with the automated search technique. This part of the tool is made up of two forms; a *Decision Specification Form* and a *GA Visualisation Module* that can be used to investigate the GA solution.

6. *Decision Specification Form*

This form enables the user to specify the scenario, and the alternatives that should be considered as feasible approaches. Once the alternatives have been determined, the level which they are taken (i.e. granularity of grouping the pipe elements) and when they can be considered, need to be defined for each of the possible alternatives.

7. *GA Visualisation Module*

This element attempts to provide the decision-maker with information regarding the GA and the ability to track the progress of the search.

10.5.2 Hierarchical Representation of a Water System Area within Software

The geographical boundaries set within this book are from the downstream point of the service reservoir to the first point of use at the customer's property boundary. These boundaries are followed within ExSoft. This part of the network, denoted within Figure 10.3 as a WSZ, can be further split into sub-zones (DMAs in England and Wales). Often performance is measured (and hence the intervention activities) at this level. The disaggregation of the costs to the DMAs is dealt with within the software using simple allocation rules. Regardless of whether the area is a WSZ, DMA or some other part of the network, it is represented within the software in a similar manner.

Each area of the network is represented within the software by a set of data structures. These are;

- list of cost drivers,
- list of costs (as prescribed by the WLC spreadsheet),
- list of feasible interventions,
- list of feasible pipe interventions,
- characterisation of the pipe assets (currently by material, diameter and year laid).[2]

---

[2] The characterisation for the software and the study as a whole is limited to these variables at this stage. More complicated characterisation could be achieved. This is, however, beyond the scope of these manuals.

This data used to populate these structures is either aggregated within the MSAccess database or imported through the link with StruMap. More details of each of these data structures are provided in the subsequent sections.

The distinct hierarchical nature of the systems in England and Wales represented in Figure 10.3 can be used to demonstrate the importance of identifying at what level the decision being investigated is taken. Any piece of the network, for example a length of mains along a road, can be represented as part of a DMA, a WSZ and as an entity unto itself. Thus, when managing this piece of the network, decisions influencing it can be made at each of these levels. In fact, decisions made outside of the geographical boundaries may be overarching, therefore, influencing directly the assets themselves. It is important that it is recognised at what level a decision is being made so that its implications are accounted for.

Further to this point, taking the case of Figure 10.3 where the WSZ is split into three DMAs, there are two ways to interpret this casual link. The WSZ is an entity, as is each DMA below it. Or, a WSZ is a sum of its individual parts. The Methodology develops costs at the WSZ level, costs can be proportioned to the DMAs based on simplistic rules (i.e. based on population). The performance within a DMA will be dependent on the area itself, its make-up and the performance models themselves. Unlike the cost allocation, performance is not proportioned across the DMAs. Any deficient performance within a WSZ may be attributed to a single DMA, with all other DMAs having a performance level that is acceptable. This will mean that in the first case the resultant sum of the cost profiles of the DMAs will not be that of the WSZ. Naturally, this would be true if the WSZ is modelled as the sum of its DMAs.

It is difficult to indicate the better option out of the two. This will come down to preference being placed by the decision-maker, and the requirements being placed on the output. This point is given greater purview in Section 11.2.3.

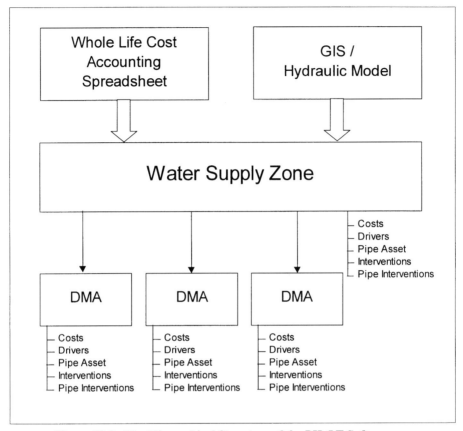

Figure 10.3: The Hierarchical Structure of the PILOT Software

10.5.3 Cost Drivers

Cost entries that are identified are separated into fixed and variable components, the latter being associated with the quantity that drives it, or its cost driver. Cost drivers, unlike the other data structures, were required to be hard coded into the software. This was necessary due to the use of the data driven models of the "Network Performance" sub-modules to project forward in time the performance of the system. It is for this reason that a number of distinctions were required when considering the cost drivers in the pilot software. Table 10.1 provides the four distinct variations in the types of cost drivers that were modelled.

Table 10.1: Modelling Cost Drivers within WLC Software

Driver Type	Explanation
Projected Primary	A continuous user-defined relationship is utilised to project the quantity into the future.
Secondary	A driver is defined as secondary if its value is assigned as a percentage of another identified cost driver.
Calculated	The measure is calculated by hard coded functionality, which is derived by user-defined relationships, or is a function of the assets that will vary with time.
Increase	The value of the driver is the incremental increase in the driver from the previous time step.

The first of the driver types discussed in Table 10.1 is generally values whose current value is known, for example, number of services supplied by the water area. This value may vary over time, depending on the change in land use over time. To reflect any temporal change, a user-defined relationship will need to be supplied. Secondary drivers are those generally reserved to situations where knowledge is lacking. For example, where a certain proportion of underground assets are known to be of a certain type, although the location of the assets in question is not known. This is often the case with lead service pipes. Calculated drivers refer to those quantities which rely on relationships developed within the "Performance Definition" to be projected temporally. An example of this is the equations utilised to project the burst behaviour of the system over the period of analysis. The final type – an increase driver – is not a cost driver *per se*, rather it indicates that the cost that has been linked to it is driven by an incremental change since the last time period. An example, that will be provided later in Chapter 11, is the cost of new consumer meters.[3]

As an example of the quantities that may be identified as cost drivers, a list of those that have been hard coded into ExSoft are given in Table 10.2. This table provides details of the units, the type of driver that they are and guidance on how the values are derived over the period of analysis.

Table 10.2: Example Cost Drivers from ExSoft

	Driver	Units	Description
1	*Accounted Volume*	MLD	Volume of accounted for water.
2	*Base Complaints*	Number	The number of complaints per year that can be expected to be received regardless of the actions taken.
3	*Burst Number*	Number	Number of burst events experienced by the pipes. Projected through the relationships described.
4	*Consumers*	Number	Number of service connections.

---

[3] The average meter coverage in England and Wales in 2000 was 14%. This value ranges significantly, with one company having up to 60% coverage. However, the role of meters in demand management has been recognised, therefore the meter uptake is expected to increase with time. Obviously, there exists an associated cost with it.

5	*Consumer Leakage Volume*	MLD	Leakage volume that is attributed to service pipes. It has been assumed with the software that this is a secondary driver associated with the *Leakage Volume*.
6	*Customers Interrupted*	Number	Number of customers who experience an interruption.
7	*Lead Service Pipes*	Number (%)	It has been assumed that the location of the lead service pipes within the zone is unknown, if in fact the actual number is itself known. Therefore, the cost driver *Lead Service Pipes* has been made a secondary driver associated with the *Consumers* driver.
8	*Metre Ferrous Mains*	Metres	Total length of ferrous mains within the water area.
9	*Metre Mains*	Metres	Total length of mains within the water area.
10	*NRR Consumer Leakage*	L/prop/ hr/yr	Expected natural rate of rise in the leakage observed in the consumer/service pipes.

To demonstrate the differences of these driver types, an example is provided based around the complaints module and how it is handled within ExSoft. The number of complaints within a water area are split between a base load (*Base Complaints*) and those that result from incidents. In the various performance modules within the "Network Definition" module, only one type of incident is modelled, namely mains bursts (*Burst Number*). Both the base load and the number of complaints associated with a main burst (*Complaint Per Burst*) are defined as cost drivers.[4] Thus the total number of complaints can be calculated at any time step using Equation 10.1;

Complaints = Base Complaints + Burst Number · Complaints Per Burst   (10.1)

The total costs of complaints (and investigations) can thus be derived from the value resulting from Equation 10.1 multiplied by the unit cost. The total cost of complaints (including investigations), in line with Section 4.5.1.8, is then required to be separated across three elements; normal supply, bursts and leakage. This is achieved by providing secondary drivers that enable the total complaints to be allocated across these elements, namely, *Burst Complaints*, *Normal Complaints* and *Leakage Complaints*.

Both the calculation of the complaints, and the allocation to the various cost elements is given pictorially in Figure 10.4.

---

[4] Defining these values as cost drivers allows, where appropriate, the propensity of the consumers to complain in future to be accounted for.

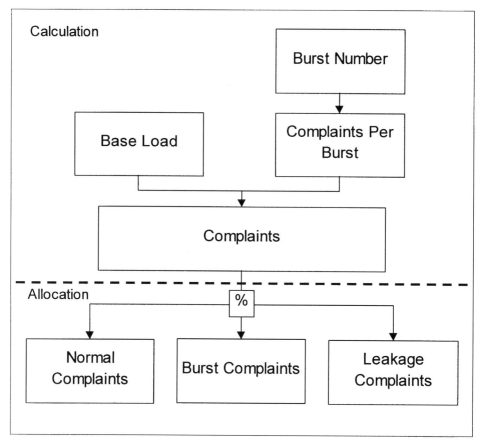

Figure 10.4: Consideration of complaints within the PILOT software

10.5.4 Cost Structures

Costs are modelled within ExSoft through the use of data structures that provide the functionality to consider the various cost/driver interrelationships defined within the "WLC Accounting" module. For example, the WLC accounting module distinguishes costs, firstly between private and social costs and secondly between fixed and variable costs. This is reflected in the fields of the cost element defined in Table 10.3. Other fields included within the table are the identification of the driver and two that are utilised to define target based costs such as regulatory penalties. The cost equation field of Table 10.3 provides the name of a table within the linked MSAccess database that defines a step-like cost relationship with a certain driver value. This cost is considered over and above the fixed and variable costs, with the cost itself assumed to be a private cost. The "Time Target Table" field defines a table name (also included within the MSAccess database) that can be used to set the performance targets, from where it is deemed necessary to derive regulatory penalties.

When considering costs over extended periods it may be necessary to consider the likely efficiency gains over this period due to technological advances. Modelling efficiency gains is achieved through defining continuous unit functions.[5] It has been assumed for ExSoft that only fixed and variable costs are factored by this efficiency factor. It seems counter-intuitive to apply efficiency costs to social costs, although it may be perceived as an option to use inverse unit functions to allow such costs to increase with time (i.e. increasing efficiency equation) to reflect increasing accountability of a company's activities.

Table 10.3: The Fields in a Cost Element in the WLC Accounting Module

Variable	Description
Name	Name of the intervention.
Private Fixed	Annual fixed private cost associated with the intervention.
Social Fixed	Annual fixed social cost associated with the intervention.
Private Variable	Variable private cost per unit of the identified driver.
Social Variable	Variable or social cost per unit of the identified driver.
Variable Driver	Cost Driver identified within the WLC Accounting that drives the variable costs.
Cost Equation	Provides the table name within the MSAccess database which provides the information for the function that defines a step-like relationship between a fixed cost and a given driver value. When a target table is also provided, the cost then becomes a function of whether the target is met.
Time Target Table	Provides the name of a table within the MSAccess database that provides targets that the cost driver quantity must not exceed. These targets can, where appropriate, vary with time.

10.5.4.1   Cost Types

A requirement of the England and Wales RAG guidelines is the provision of a distribution of network costs allocated to three main activities; normal supply, burst and leakage. The facility has been provided in the software to carry this through the analysis by the setting up of data structures known as cost types. Differentiation is made for the imported costs through searching for keywords in the names utilised for each imported cost. These keywords are hard coded in, namely "Leakage" and "Burst". Any costs whose name (as specified in the relevant field in Table 10.3) has the keyword "Leakage" in it is allocated to the cost type "Leakage". Similarly with the keyword "Burst". All other costs are attributed to "Normal Supply". This allows the pilot software to develop WLC accounts following the RAG guidelines for the studied network.

10.5.5 Operational Interventions

The term interventions is used within the Methodology to denote any managed activity that will have an effect on the performance of the system, or on an attribute

---

[5] A unit function has a range of 0 to 1.

that is identified as a driver for one of the input costs. In the software, a distinction is made between actions on the pipe assets (e.g. pipe replacement) to those on the system as a whole (e.g. change in leakage control strategy). This section deals with the latter, with pipe interventions dealt with in Section 10.5.6.

Details of the interventions are brought in through the MSAccess database. Interventions need to be defined in terms of the cost of the activity and its effect on the network. Table 10.4 provides the details of the fields used to define an intervention in the pilot software. The three fields of "Effect On", "Effect Type" and "Effect" in Table 10.4 define the effect on the network by the intervention. Firstly, the driver that is affected by the intervention needs to be identified. Two alternatives are provided to define the effect, either as a percentage reduction or in absolute terms. The last field quantifies this effect. An intervention is considered similar to the other costs, hence it incorporates the functionality of the cost structure.

Table 10.4: Field Details for the Operational Intervention Types

Variable	Type	Description
Name	Text	Name of the intervention.
Effect On	Text	Nominates the cost driver (attribute/performance) that the intervention has an effect on.
Effect Type	Integer	Nominates the type of effect - 0 - as a percentage or 1 - absolute.
Effect	Double	The effect that the intervention has on the driver.
Private Fixed	Double	Fixed private cost associated with the intervention.
Social Fixed	Double	Fixed social cost associated with the intervention.
Private Variable	Double	Variable private cost associated with the intervention.
Social Variable	Double	Variable social cost associated with the intervention.
Variable Driver	Text	Cost Driver that drives the variable costs attributed to the intervention.

10.5.6 Pipe Interventions

Interventions that act upon the individual pipe elements of the network are differentiated from the operational interventions. This distinction is made on two fronts, the variation in costs that is witnessed for various diameter sized mains and the fact that interventions may occur on any percentage of the mains within a water area. Secondly, like the costs, the effect that a pipe intervention type has on the performance of the system is a function of the length of the piping system that experiences the intervention. Table 10.5 provides the variation in the fields of the MSAccess table that brings in the information for the various pipe intervention types. The "Diameter Table" field provides a MSAccess table name that stores the necessary information for the varying cost with diameter sizes.

Table 10.5: Field Details for the Pipe Intervention Types

Variable	Type	Description
Name	Text	Name of the pipe intervention.
Material	Text	Name of the material used in the pipe intervention.
Table Name	Text	Table that stipulates the variation of the fixed private cost with the length of the pipe intervention. This can be used if economies of scale are to be considered.
Diameter Table	Text	Table that stipulates the variation in the variable costs for various diameters.
Primary Effect On	Text	Nominates the cost driver (attribute/performance) that the pipe intervention will effect.
Primary Effect Type	Integer	Nominates the type of effect. Unlike interventions, two extra cases are supplied which enable the effect to be defined in terms of % of pipes intervened. The options available are:- 0. percentage decrease in the current driver level which occurs when a pipe is intervened, 1. absolute decrease in the current driver level which occurs when a pipe is intervened, 2. a percentage decrease in the current level based on the percentage length of mains intervened, 3. absolute decrease based on the percentage of length of mains intervened.
Primary Effect	Double	The effect that the intervention has on the driver. This value only requires an input if the Primary Effect Type field is set to either 0 or 1.
Primary Effect Equation Type	Integer	Equation type that defines the relationship between the % of the pipe length that is intervened and the effect on the identified cost driver. This along with the relevant K coefficients only are required to be defined if the Primary Effect Type is defined as either 2 or 3.
Primary Equation K0	Double	Equation K0 value.
Primary Equation K1	Double	Equation K1 value.
Primary Equation K2	Double	Equation K2 value.
Primary Equation K3	Double	Equation K3 value.
Private Fixed	Double	Annual fixed private cost associated with the pipe intervention.

Social Fixed	Double	Annual fixed social cost associated with the pipe intervention.
Private Variable	Double	Variable private cost associated with the pipe intervention.
Social Variable	Double	Variable social cost associated with the pipe intervention.
Variable Driver	Text	Cost Driver that drives the variable costs attributed to the intervention. It is assumed in the case of pipe interventions that the variable costs are per metre, therefore this field does not require input.

10.5.7 Storing the Pipe Asset Information within the Software

ExSoft imports the pipe asset data through the StruMap link. The pipe asset information is stored in two formats. Firstly, the pipe elements are characterised in terms of the material, diameter and year laid. The primary characterisation is undertaken in terms of the material. This characterisation provides the ability to track the changing asset stock throughout the period of analysis. If the hydraulic performance is to be explicitly included in the analysis it may be necessary to represent each pipe element in the software.

10.5.8 Integrating the Data Structures

Three distinct data structures have been discussed in this section that underpin the Methodology. Figure 10.5 provides a diagrammatic view of how these elements interact. In the top left hand corner are the interventions (or pipe interventions). They are defined in two respects, the effect they have on the system which is accounted for when updating the values of the cost drivers and their cost which is updated in the WLC accounts. The effect the interventions have on the cost drivers is accounted for in the cost structures, through updating the variable costs and where appropriate the penalty costs. Once updated these costs are passed through to the WLC accounts. This process is undertaken throughout the period of analysis.

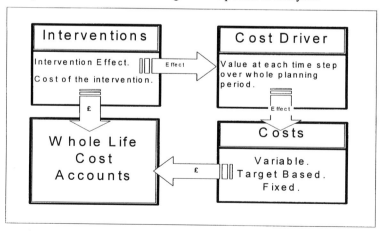

Figure 10.5: Interplay between the Major Data Structures within the WLC Methodology

10.5.9 Operational Data

It is not appropriate to associate all the relationships required by the performance modules with the water area. Many relationships are required to model the deterioration of the pipe assets, which are modelled utilising company wide (i.e. area non-specific) data. For example, the burst relationships were derived from historical data that was aggregated to enable their identification, and then disaggregated to provide details for specific areas. In line with this, the pilot software does not associate these relationships with particular areas rather they are defined globally and adjusted for local effects unaccounted for in the data analysis. The relationships defined for these factors are brought in through the link with the MSAccess database. Relationships for the hydraulic deterioration in the mains and the expected customer interruptions are also imported through the MSAccess database.

CHAPTER ELEVEN
Scenario Management Case Study

11.1   Introduction

The book to this point has provided a theoretical background on WLC, its development into a Methodology for application to a water distribution network, the constituent elements that it is built upon and their integration onto a decision support platform. This chapter focusses on the application of a case study within this decision support platform, providing the results attained from a WLC analysis.

A case study system utilising representative data from an actual system in the UK,[1] was imported into ExSoft. This chapter steps through the population of ExSoft with data, presenting where appropriate this data that is imported. Once consolidated within ExSoft, the example provides a basis to demonstrate many of the concepts introduced for the "Decision Tool" module in Chapters 9 and 10.

The decision support encompassed within ExSoft was developed along two level concepts. Chapter 11 concentrates on the first level. For this purpose, ExSoft provides the user with the ability to observe the effect of various operational and pipe interventions on network performance and the WLC. The scheduling of these operational and maintenance activities are limited to user-defined, examples of which are given within. Chapter 12 will move on and provide details of the automated decision making level provided by ExSoft.

11.2   Case Study

The case study application is for a small WSZ consisting of two DMAs serving around 2000 customers in total (population ~5000). The WSZ comprises 24 kilometres of water mains, predominantly cast iron, dating as far back as 1920, with the majority laid in the 1930s and 1940s.

A StruMap hydraulic model of the network was prepared. In addition to the data required for a hydraulic analysis (diameter, roughness coefficient, length) each pipe also had its year laid and material type assigned. These pipe attributes are required for the structural performance modules. Data from the collaborating water companies were consolidated and evaluated so that the various input tables in the MSAccess database were populated. Of the cost drivers identified for the case study not modelled by the "Performance Definition" module, only one was identified to vary with time.

---

[1] The material and year laid distributions were representative of the respective distributions as recorded at the end of 1999.

This is the "Accounted Volume" portion, including amongst others, the consumer demand portion of the distribution input.

The "WLC Accounting" module as described in Chapter 5 was populated using representative costs for a WSZ of the size considered here. These costs are provided in Table 11.1, the columns of which follow those identified in Table 10.3. The exception are the last two columns. The text within these columns identifies tables within the MSAccess database that define step-like functions that link a cost with a set range of values of the cost driver. These tables are utilised for the regulatory penalties.

Before presenting the results in this section it needs to be highlighted that the profiles provided assume that no pipe interventions occur over the period of analysis. Therefore, the cost profiles will reflect the deteriorating performance that accompanies no maintenance activity. Operational Interventions, due to their ongoing nature have been assumed to continue over the period of analysis. Section 11.3 highlights the effects of changing these operational interventions. Section 11.4 will concentrate on the effect of scheduling Pipe Interventions on the cost and cost driver profiles.

Resultant of a WLC analysis is the generation of cost profiles over the period of analysis. These cost profiles represent a set of accounts, which themselves can be disaggregated. A common disaggregation throughout this book has been between the private and social costs. As such Figure 11.1 also provides private and social cost profiles. As can be seen, over the period of analysis, there is much increase in the private costs. This significant increase is primarily due to the "regulatory penalty" costs. These costs represent the consequences of not supplying the required service to customers (i.e. DG2 penalty, DG3 penalty and burst penalty in Table 11.1). This effect can be best witnessed in Figure 11.2, which disaggregates the private costs into the direct operating costs and the "regulatory penalty" costs. The gradual increase seen in the operating cost profile in Figure 11.2 indicates that the primary justification for mains renewal will come from the regulatory penalties associated with deteriorating service levels. This is not to say that there are no economic incentives for mains renewal, it is more likely that the increases in operating costs are being masked by the huge overheads associated with the at-boundary on-costs. These costs currently are considered as fixed costs (see the "Fixed Private Cost" column in Table 11.1), as it is nearly impossible to link such costs to the activities within a single WSZ within a large company. This though may change if the Methodology was applied across larger geographical boundaries, in which case distinction may be made on where these activities occur.

Regulatory Accounting Guidelines 4.01 (Ofwat, 1992) stipulates that the operating costs should be allocated to "Normal Operation", "Bursts" and "Leakage". This differentiation is made through the "Cost Types" data structures introduced in Section 10.5.4.1. The allocation of the direct costs across these three "Cost Types" is shown in Figure 11.3. The need to do such an allocation exercise is completely regulatory driven in England and Wales. How it is achieved within each company may vary. The structure of the costs brought into ExSoft should reflect any such variation that exists on the distribution of costs across these cost types. For example, the user has the choice of allocating the cost of the water lost due to leakage to either "Leakage" or "Normal Operation". The costs provided in Table 11.1 are based on the former choice. The costs in Table 11.1 include "Leakage Cost of Water", "Raw Water and

Treatment" and "Treated Water". The driver for the "Leakage Cost of Water" is the **Leakage Volume**. The driver for the other two costs is identified as the **Accounted Volume**. Also note that the private variable cost of the "Leakage Cost of Water" is the sum of the other two. The use of the term "Leakage" in the name allows ExSoft to attribute the cost to the user's specifications.

Table 11.1: An Example of Cost Table Input for a WSZ (all costs are £ p.a.)

Name	Private Fixed	Social Fixed	Private Variable	Social Variable	Variable Driver	Table Name	Time Target Table
Bacteriological Risk			0.0003	0.00003	Metre Ferrous Mains		
Burst Complaints	780.98		17.96	0	Burst Complaints		
Burst Congestion				5.38	Burst Number		
Burst Cost of Repairs	10919.64		1	0.1	Burst Cost		
Burst Image Costs		0	100	0	Burst Number	Burst Image	
Burst Net Losses				0	Customers		
Burst WTP				0.01	Customers		
Bursts Regulatory					Burst Number	Burst Penalty	
Byelaw Inspection	3000		20	0	Inspections		
Complaints	7607.12		17.96	0	Normal Complaints		
Consumer Meters	3000		50	0	Increase Consumer Meters		
DG2 Regulatory					DG2 Failures	DG2 Penalty	
DG3 Regulatory					DG3 Failures	DG3 Penalty	
Interruption Cost			10	7.34	Customer Interruption Hours		
Iron Removal			0.0015	0.00015	Consumers		
Iron Risk			0.002	0.0002	Metre Ferrous Mains		
Leakage Complaints	346.72		17.96	0	Leakage Complaints		
Leakage Confidence				0.01	Customers		

Name	Private Fixed	Social Fixed	Private Variable	Social Variable	Variable Driver	Table Name	Time Target Table
Leakage Cost of Water			97.5	0	Leakage Volume		
Leakage Detection	4709.82	0	0	0			
Leakage Image Costs		0	100	0	Leakage Volume	Leakage Image	
Leakage Regulatory					Leakage Volume	Leakage	Leakage Target
Leakage WTP				0.01	Customers		
Operation & Control	14000		0	0			
PAH Risk			0.00166	0.00017	Metre Coal Tar Lining		
Phosphate	0	0	0.2	0	Volume Water		
Raw Water & Treatment	4593.2	0	95	0	Accounted Volume		
Replace & Repair Meters	3000		60	0	Meter Repairs		
Sediment Cleaning		0	0.0015	0.00015	Consumers		
Supply	39830.53						
THM Risk			0.0003	0.00003	Metre Ferrous Mains		
Treated Water	2504	0	2.5	0	Accounted Volume		

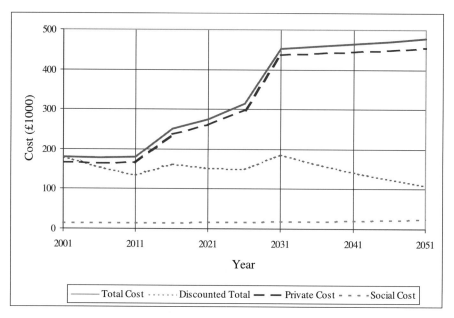

Figure 11.1: 50 Year Private/Social Cost Profile for the Case Study

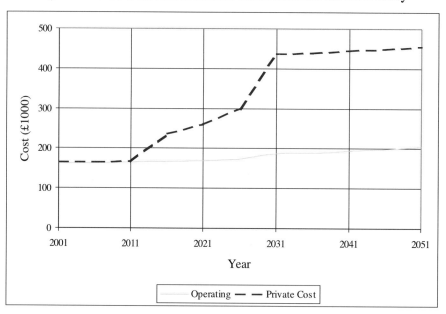

Figure 11.2: 50 Year Operating/Private Cost Profile for the Case Study

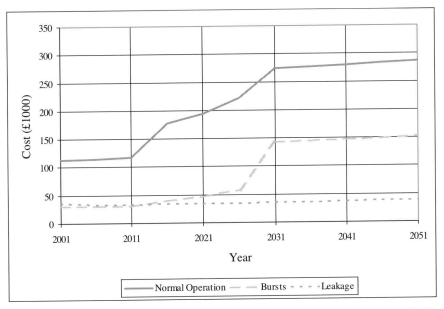

Figure 11.3: 50 Year Normal Operation/Bursts/Leakage Cost Profile for the Case Study

11.2.1 Cost Drivers with Associated Penalties

The increases in the costs seen in Figures 11.1 to 11.3 are associated with the penalties incurred due to deteriorating service levels. The England and Wales regulatory regime places emphasis on the following drivers, which have explicitly been identified in Table 11.1 with associated penalties;

- Extent of low pressure problems (DG2): Number of properties at risk from receiving unacceptably low pressure,

- Scale of interruptions of supplies to customers (DG3): Unplanned interruptions to supplies greater than 12 hours,

- Number of bursts,

- Leakage Volume.

The profiles for these four measures over the period of analysis are provided in Figure 11.4. The penalty costs assigned to the deteriorating performance are also provided. It is worth noting for the leakage curve that no penalty cost has been assigned. This is for two reasons. Firstly, as will be seen in Section 11.3, this level of leakage has been driven down by operational interventions that drive the level of leakage down over the period of analysis. Secondly, unlike the other cost drivers in Figure 11.4, a target is set for leakage.[2] This can been seen in the "Leakage Regulatory" cost entry of Table 11.1, where a "Time Target Table" has been defined. This table defines a target of 0.2 MLD over the period of analysis. As can be seen in Figure 11.4(b) the leakage level never moves above the defined target.

---

[2] Unlike the other measures, leakage is not a serviceability measure, therefore, the defined target becomes a variable.

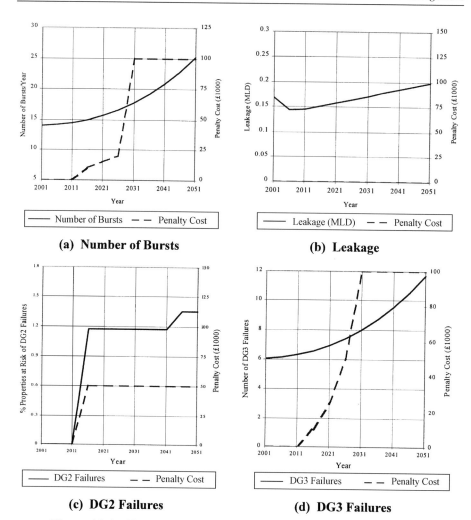

(a) Number of Bursts

(b) Leakage

(c) DG2 Failures

(d) DG3 Failures

Figure 11.4: 50 Year Profiles for Drivers with Associated Penalties

11.2.2 Other Cost Drivers

The cost drivers identified in 11.2.1 are only those that have associated penalty costs. There are numerous cost entries in Table 10.1 that have been linked with drivers. Rather than going through all such drivers, focus is placed on those drivers that are calculated through the performance evaluation methods detailed in Chapters 6 through 8. Figure 11.5 presents examples of "Accounted Volume" (Figure 11.5a), "Customers Interrupted" and "Customer Interruption Hours" (Figure 11.5b), "Normal Complaints", "Burst Complaints" and "Leakage Complaints" (Figure 11.5c).

These profiles indicate the deteriorating service provided over the period of analysis. The subsequent increases in the operating costs would thus be picked, and are displayed in cost profiles of Figure 11.1 through 11.3.

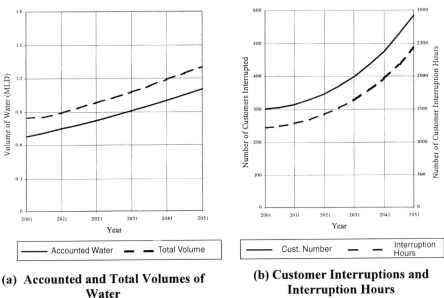

(a) **Accounted and Total Volumes of Water**

(b) **Customer Interruptions and Interruption Hours**

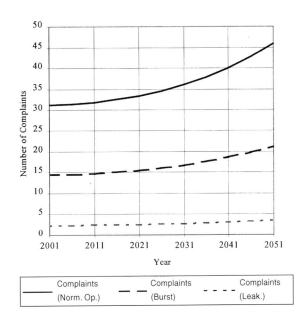

(c) **Complaints within water area**

Figure 11.5: 50 Year Profiles for Drivers without Associated Penalties

11.2.3 Hierarchical Structure

Section 10.5.2 highlighted that the Methodology was set up on the basis that a WSZ is an entity as is each DMA within it, rather than the sum of its individual DMAs. The differentiation between these two cases can be best seen for the case study through the cost profiles in Figure 11.6. The cost profile for the WSZ is not identical to the sum of the cost profiles for the constituent DMAs. The costs are imported at WSZ level and along with the required targets, are proportioned across the DMA using simple allocation rules. This proportioning is based on the number of customers in the example. Therefore, the penalty costs assigned to a given performance level within a DMA is a proportion of that applied for the WSZ. If the deterioration in the areas was the same, then each DMA would incur the subsequent regulatory penalties at the same time. Thus the proportioning of the regulatory penalties would have no effect. However, the deterioration within the constituent DMAs varies depending on the make-up of the water area in question. Thus, the penalties associated with deteriorating performance at a single DMA (assuming all other DMAs meet the required performance) would be a proportion to that applied at the WSZ level. This is witnessed in Figure 11.6 through the smoothing of the curve that represents the sum of the DMAs compared to that which represents the WSZ as a separate entity.

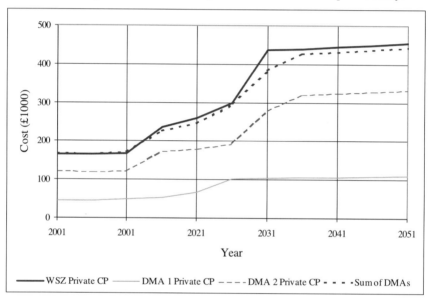

Figure 11.6: 50 Year Cost Profiles for Different Operational Hierarchical Levels

11.3   Applying Operational Interventions on the Case Study Water Area

Operational interventions that are included as decision variables in the WLC approach are limited to effects on leakage. As an example, four activities have been identified that mitigate the quantity of water lost within a network. These are;

1. pressure reduction,

2. normal leakage detection (which includes nightline monitoring),

3. detection and repair services to customers,

4. additional inspection (a more proactive approach where teams are sent out to find leaks).

Each of these activities has an associated cost and an effect on leakage volume. The leakage performance module differentiates between the leakage within the distribution mains and that with the service pipes. Activity 1 has an effect on both of these sources. Activities such as 2 and 4 affect the leakage within the distribution mains, whilst Activity 3 will reduce the leakage in the service pipes. The actual reduction in leakage experienced due to each activity can be obtained from the analysis of leakage operational data and through discussions with the operational staff. Such analyses will have been an integral part of previous estimates of the "economic level of leakage" required in England and Wales.

For the example provided here the following parameters were assumed for the leakage performance module:

- Initial Leakage Volume = 0.169 MLD,

- Leakage was allocated: 75% Distribution Mains, 25% Consumer Pipes,

- NRR of Leakage in distribution mains: 2 l/property/hr/yr, which was linked to pipe age. The NRR varied at 0.03 l/property/hour/year/year of main age.

- A constant NRR of Leakage in the service pipes of: 0.5 l/property/hour/year.

Figure 11.7 shows the projected total leakage levels for a combination of the four activities detailed above. Each of the interventions will have an associated cost that is dependent on the required resources for the activity. Another way to drive down leakage is mains renewal.[3] Section 11.4 details the effect of pipe interventions on leakage levels.

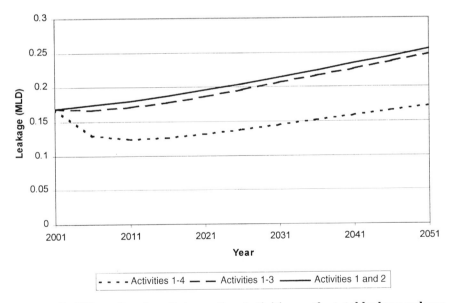

Figure 11.7: Effect of various Intervention Activities on the total leakage volume over the period of analysis

---

[3] The common thinking in England and Wales is that leakage alone is not a driver for mains renewal at present. Mains renewal is driven by water compliance or maintaining serviceability.

11.4   Applying Pipe Interventions on the Case Study Water Area

Beyond operational interventions, the other major maintenance activities on distribution networks are interventions on the pipe infrastructure. In the example, only one pipe intervention type has been considered, the replacement of the mains with an equivalent sized MDPE pipe. Only simple pipe schedules are undertaken here, to highlight the effect that pipe interventions have on the performance of the network that have associated regulatory penalties and hence WLC stream. This though quickly highlights the scope for utilising search techniques that can automate the routine thus eliminating the human resources required to fine tune the operational and maintenance schedule.

As an example, all of the CI 100 mm are scheduled to be replaced immediately. This results in the cost streams provided in Figure 11.8. An extra cost type has been included in this figure, namely, the capital cost associated with the scheduled pipe replacement. This has been included as a step function for clarity. In its current form the WLC software does not decide when, within a five year period, the replacement has occurred. Therefore, this cost is allocated and proportioned evenly across the time step rather than as a single point cost. This follows how the other costs are reported.

A comparison between the cost streams provided in Figures 11.8 and 11.1 indicates that apart from this initial capital expenditure, the cost curves throughout the period of analysis are different. This difference is best witnessed through Figure 11.9 that makes a comparison between the regulatory penalties allocated to the cost streams of Figures 11.8 and 11.1. Clearly, the pipe intervention delays the regulatory penalties being incurred. A breakdown of the regulatory penalty costs can be seen in Figure 11.10. Like Figure 11.4, this figure provides each of the cost drivers that has an associated regulatory penalty. It implies that further pipe interventions are required throughout the time horizon to ensure that network performance is sustained.

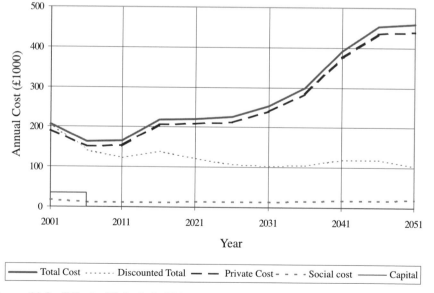

Figure 11.8: Effect of Scheduled Pipe Intervention Activities on the 50 Year Cost Profiles

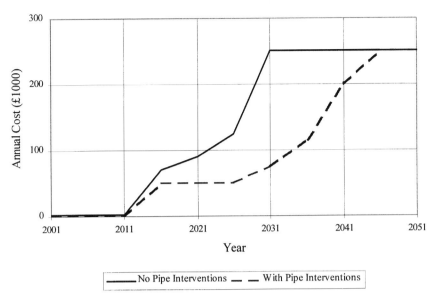

Figure 11.9: Effect of Scheduled Pipe Intervention Activities on the 50 Year Cost Profiles

Sections 11.4 and 11.5 provide details of the cost streams and performance of the network. They allow, as in Figure 11.7, the effect of different intervention strategies on performance to be observed, assimilating all interactions onto a single platform. However, they do not provide the alternative that provides the least whole life cost. Another example provided in Figure 11.11 illustrates this. In this example, all CI 100 mm mains in the water supply zone are replaced at time step 0. On top of this, all CI 75 mm mains are scheduled for replacement in the time step starting 2021. The extra set of mains scheduled for replacement also significantly reduces the cost streams. However, this will not be the best arrangement. Figure 11.11 does not address whether higher or lower levels of leakage detection are necessary given the pipe interventions. Also, further pipe interventions may lower the cost profiles over the period of analysis, either through further delaying the regulatory penalties, or through efficiency savings.

To provide further decision support in this respect, the decision tool has incorporated the search technique that automates the generation and assessment of various scenarios. This will be investigated in Chapter 12.

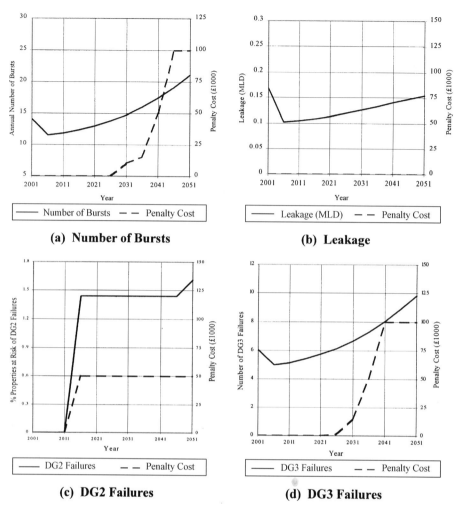

(a) Number of Bursts   **(b) Leakage**

(c) DG2 Failures   **(d) DG3 Failures**

**Figure 11.10: 50 Year Profiles for Drivers with Associated Penalties after a
Single Pipe Intervention**

11.5   Reporting WLC Analyses

Reporting a WLC analysis over the period of analysis, due to the amount of
information generated can become an onerous task.   Until now only graphical
representations of the cost streams or performance measures have been presented.
These results can also be presented as a set of accounts. In implementing ExSoft it
was determined that the accounts should be prepared for two distinct time horizons.
One supplies accounts for the full set of entries for a particular time step, the other
provides a summary of the costs for each cost type over the period of analysis.

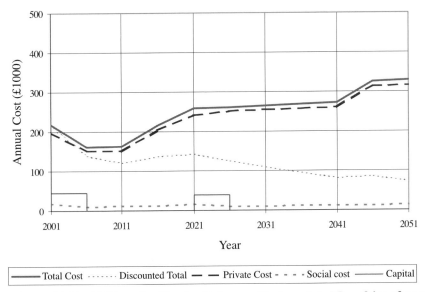

Figure 11.11: 50 Year Profiles for Drivers with Associated Penalties after a Multiple Pipe Intervention

The first set of accounts for the first time step for the case study system are provided in Table 11.2 (once again assuming no pipe interventions). In other words, these accounts are the breakdown of the left most point on the cost stream of Figures 11.1 through 11.3. All entries of the WLC Accounts, in line with Table 11.1, are detailed and separated into the three primary cost types ("Normal Supply", "Leakage", "Bursts"). The costs provided in these tables are based on the initial values of the cost drivers, and the current performance of the system. Similarly, these accounts could be generated over the period of analysis, tracking where the increases in costs accrue.

Closer inspection of Table 11.2 indicates that the various operational interventions have been accounted for under the "Leakage" cost type. Operational interventions, unlike pipe interventions are classed within RAG 4.01 as operating costs and must be accrued as such. The accounts displayed in Table 11.2 assume no capital maintenance and as such, no capital expenditure is seen on the accounts.

The second set of accounts that can be generated by ExSoft provide a summary over the period of analysis through reporting just the cost types. These accounts are provided in Table 11.3, with the values provided graphically in Figures 11.1 through 11.3. As with the accounts displayed in Table 11.2, no pipe interventions are scheduled. As such no capital maintenance appears within the accounts.

Table 11.2: The WLC Accounts for the Period 0-5 years for the WSZ (all costs are £1000 p.a.)

	Private	Social	Total
Routine	**104.18**	**9.08**	**113.26**
Bac Risk	0.01	0.00	0.01
Byelaw Inspection	3.24	0.00	3.24
Complaints	8.17	0.00	8.17
Consumer Meters	3.00	0.00	3.00
DG2 Regulatory	0.00	0.00	0.00
DG3 Regulatory	0.06	0.00	0.06
Interruption Cost	0.00	9.02	9.02
Iron Removal	0.31	0.03	0.34
Iron Risk	0.04	0.00	0.04
Operation & Control	14.00	0.00	14.00
PAH Risk	0.00	0.00	0.00
Phosphate	0.06	0.00	0.06
Raw Water & Treatment	28.03	0.00	28.03
Replace & Repair Meters	4.01	0.00	4.01
Sediment Cleaning	0.31	0.03	0.34
Supply	39.83	0.00	39.83
THM Risk	0.01	0.00	0.01
Treated Water Cost	3.12	0.00	3.12
Water Supply Zone	0.00	0.00	0.00

	Private	Social	Total
Burst	**26.25**	**1.49**	**27.74**
Burst Complaints	0.81	0.00	0.81
Burst Congestion Cost	0.00	0.08	0.08
Burst Cost of Repairs	24.81	1.39	26.19
Burst Image Costs	0.64	0.00	0.64
Burst Net Losses	0.00	0.00	0.00
Burst WTP	0.00	0.02	0.02
Bursts Regulatory	0.00	0.00	0.00
Leakage	**26.96**	**2.98**	**29.94**
Leakage (Passive)	4.71	0.00	4.71
Leakage Complaints	0.39	0.00	0.39
Leakage Confidence	0.00	0.02	0.02
Leakage Cost of Water	6.01	0.00	6.01
Leakage Image Costs	0.81	0.00	0.81
Leakage Regulatory	0.00	0.00	0.00
Leakage WTP	0.00	0.02	0.02
Additional Inspection	4.00	2.14	6.14
Pressure Reduction	1.00	0.10	1.10
Detection and Repair Service	3.00	0.00	3.00
Normal Leakage detection	7.04	0.70	7.74

Table 11.3: The WLC Accounts by Cost Types over the Period of Analysis for the WSZ (all costs are £1000 p.a.)

Cost Type	Years (Time Steps 1 through 10)										
	0-5	5-10	10-15	15-20	20-25	25-30	30-35	35-40	40-45	45-50	50-55
Private Costs by Type											
Supply	104.18	106.39	116.68	123.03	184.45	210.95	262.53	264.20	265.96	267.81	269.76
Burst	26.25	27.49	27.88	37.44	43.70	54.69	139.94	141.48	143.32	145.51	148.05
Leakage	26.96	24.99	24.78	24.88	25.08	25.31	25.56	25.82	26.09	26.40	27.12
Regulatory	0.06	2.06	11.06	25.07	90.07	125.08	250.08	250.09	250.10	250.11	250.12
Social Costs by Type											
Supply	9.08	9.29	9.61	10.06	10.65	11.41	12.35	13.50	14.86	16.45	18.30
Burst	1.49	1.51	1.55	1.61	1.69	1.79	1.92	2.08	2.27	2.50	2.77
Leakage	2.98	2.98	2.98	2.98	2.98	2.98	2.98	2.98	2.98	2.98	2.98
Regulatory	0.00	0.00	0.00	0.00	0.00	0.00	0.00	0.00	0.00	0.00	0.00
Total Costs by Type											
Supply	113.26	115.68	126.28	133.08	195.10	222.36	274.88	277.69	280.81	284.26	288.06
Burst	27.74	29.00	29.43	39.05	45.39	56.48	141.86	143.56	145.59	148.01	150.82
Leakage	29.94	27.97	27.76	27.86	28.06	28.29	28.54	28.80	29.07	29.38	30.10
Regulatory	0.06	2.06	11.06	25.07	90.07	125.08	250.08	250.09	250.10	250.11	250.12
Total Costs for Area											
	171.00	174.71	194.53	225.05	358.61	432.21	695.37	700.14	705.58	711.75	719.09

CHAPTER TWELVE
Automating the Decision Making Process

12.1 Introduction

ExSoft provides decision support at two levels. Chapter 11 discussed the first level of decision support, where the decision-maker can calculate the whole life cost of a water distribution network for user defined scenarios. Although it allows a user to observe the change in the WLC for various scenarios and operating/maintenance strategies, it only provides the user with a single value for the WLC. No indication is given on whether a cost profile represents the "best one" for the scenario being investigated. Water distribution networks with their distributed assets imply that there are countless alternatives that meet the performance objectives. Different maintenance alternatives are available for an asset group, each with an effect on the different performance aspects of the system. Search techniques allow the decision making process to be automated, allowing the investigation of these many thousand different strategies to meet the defined objective. From these scenarios the "best" is identified. Chapter 12 details the implementation of an automated search mechanism to identify the "optimal operating/maintenance option".

In using any automated search techniques the user must be aware of their limitations, situations where they should be used and when not. There is a universal recognition that the confidence in these techniques is dependent on the information being provided. It is for this reason that the decision support was developed in two stages. Confidence must be built up in the information being imported. Often this information is deficient, requiring judgement on the part of the decision-maker. However, once this understanding and confidence is established, the scenario management component of the decision making process can be automated. This allows the full implications of the reliance on engineering judgement to be seen through to their performance and financial conclusions. It is for this reason that the use of an automated decision tool should be an iterative process. Knowledge generated should be fed back into the first level, allowing any judgements made by the decision-maker to be refined. Equally, the findings may enable priorities for the allocation of resources to data collection to enable the more sensitive relationships to be firmed up.

Automating a decision making process requires all aspects of the decision being made to be explicitly defined. To achieve this end, there exists a process to enable decisions to be implemented. Section 12.2 outlines these steps, paying particular reference to the application of the Methodology. The chosen search technique in ExSoft is the genetic algorithm (GA). As such, the views presented within Chapter 12 are in respect of this algorithm. Although it is recognised that alternative techniques exist, the GA was chosen due to its flexibility in its application to a wide variety of problems both in academia and within industry across the world.

12.2   Steps in Automating the Decision Making Process

In automating a decision making process a decision-maker is placing control of the process to a computer. Thus the decision and the alternative strategies to meet this objective need to be defined. Table 12.1 provides the three distinct steps to fulfil this. The first step is to stipulate the objective[1] (including constraints) that is sought through applying the process. An example is to, say, minimise the WLC throughout the period of analysis. Once this has been determined it is necessary to identify what activities can be undertaken to achieve this objective. For example, activities can be undertaken on the assets that make up the fabric of the network. These activities and/or assets represent the decision variables in the problem. The last step in the process is to identify the various alternative activities available for each of the decision variables. For pipe assets this may include the various rehabilitation techniques available.

An extra dimension is added to the decision making process due to the temporal nature of the Methodology. Activities can be undertaken at discrete intervals within the period of analysis or can be undertaken continuously throughout. It will be necessary to attain an appreciation of how the activity in question is undertaken in the field.

Table 12.1: Steps in Automating the Decision Making Process

Step:	Action:	Comment:
1	Define Objective	What the process ultimately wants to achieve.
2	Identify Decisions	Actions that can be taken throughout the planning horizons.
3	Identify Alternatives	Alternatives that can be undertaken for each action identified in Step 2.

An important consideration when defining the alternatives for the various decision variables is that an increase in their number increases the complexity of the problem. This will have implications in terms of the computational time and the quality of the final strategy identified by the search technique. Search techniques, although efficient, are not guaranteed to find the global optimal solution. This computational time versus quality of solution identified is a fundamental trade-off that always exists for search techniques.

12.2.1 Objective Functions and Constraints

Like classical optimisation, automated search techniques require the decision being made to be defined in terms of objective functions and constraints. Various such formulations were briefly introduced in the review of Chapter 9. These objective functions must be defined in mathematical terms. Within the Methodology the

---

[1] Planning objective and formulation have both been used to describe the objective of an optimisation problem.

simplest and most obvious objective function is that of minimising the WLC of the system over the period of analysis. This is given mathematically by Equation 12.1;

$$\text{Minimise WLC} \tag{12.1}$$

The problem is "unconstrained" due to the use of the "Regulatory Penalty" costs that translate deficient performance into monetary units. These "Regulatory Penalty" costs effectively constrain the decision within the defined targets. This is analogous to the use of constraints in classical optimisation that ensure the feasibility of the final solution. Here unfeasible solutions outside of the defined constraints are penalised accordingly.

Depending on the decision and the decision-maker's role within an organisation, constraints may need to be placed on the formulation of Equation 12.1. An example of this is where constraints are placed on the capital expenditure that can be spent in any time interval. In such cases, the decision-maker may still want to minimise the WLC given the constraints that have been placed upon him or her. Mathematically the problem formulation for this example could be given as:

$$\text{Minimise WLC}$$
$$\text{such that } Cost_{capital,i} \leq Cost_{\text{maximum capital}} \tag{12.2}$$

where, $Cost_{capital,i}$ is the capital expenditure scheduled for time step i and $Cost_{maximum\ capital}$ is the maximum capital that can be scheduled for each time step.

This problem formulation can be modelled by applying a penalty function, say $Cost_{penalty}$, to solutions that are not feasible. Therefore, the problem becomes one of minimising cost alone, i.e.

$$\text{Minimise WLC} + \sum_{i=0}^{T} \left(\left\{ \begin{array}{l} 0, \text{if } Cost_{capital,i} \leq Cost_{\text{minimumcapital}} \\ Cost_{penalty} \cdot \left(Cost_{capital,i} - Cost_{\text{minimumcapital}}\right), \text{otherwise} \end{array} \right\} \cdot \left(1+r\right)^{i \cdot 5} \right) \tag{12.3}$$

where, i is a 5-year time step, T is the number of time steps in the planning horizon and r is the discount rate. The final term in this equation defines all penalties in NPV terms. The inclusion of this term is ultimately up to the decision-maker.

It is advised that when applying values to the "Regulatory Penalty" costs within the Methodology, consideration is given to their influence within the automated search technique. These penalties constrain the objective similar to the second term on Equation 12.3, therefore, one should consider whether the applied penalties ensure that the optimisation is appropriately constrained. Undervaluation of the costs in the automated decision making process may result in infeasible solutions.

12.2.2 Decision Variables

Decision variables either relate to the assets or areas where activities can be undertaken to meet the defined objective. Within the Methodology, this represents the operational and pipe interventions. For water distribution networks, as shown in the literature review of Chapter 9 and discussed in Section 10.3, decisions can be made at various hierarchical levels to ensure that the performance of the network meets the required levels. For example, Figure 10.3 provides the distinct hierarchical set-up of a water network in England. Decisions regarding operational interventions can be made for the whole WSZ or be made for each constituent DMA. Economies of scale, available resources or personal preferences will determine the most appropriate of these two.

Decisions with respect to the pipe network presents an extra level of complexity due to its spatial distribution and connectivity. A decision can be made for the whole network, thus for all pipe elements contained therein. Alternatively, these pipe elements can be discretised into lengths of pipes, or asset groups around which decisions can be centred. There are a large number of ways that these pipe elements can be grouped, for example, one could consider each pipe element within the hydraulic model as a separate entity. Equally decisions can be made on all pipes of a given material type, say all cast iron pipes. The examples in Chapter 11 grouped pipes by material type and diameter.

12.2.3 Identify Alternatives

There are a number of alternatives available for each operational and maintenance activity. A fine distinction must be made between the available alternatives and decision variables. This is witnessed in the operational interventions identified to reduce leakage in Section 11.3. A leakage strategy may consist of any combination of these activities. Therefore, although they are alternative activities to reduce leakage within a water area, each is represented as a unique decision variable. The alternatives are whether or not to schedule the necessary resources. For the geographical scale that the Methodology is being applied to herein, this on/off assumption is justified. For larger scales of application, the levels of resources being attributed to each activity may represent the alternatives for that decision variable.

In respect of pipe elements there exists a clear difference between the decision variable and the alternatives. The decision variables are identified in line with the discussion in Section 12.2.2, whereas the alternatives amongst others are the type of rehabilitation to be undertaken, i.e. replacement, structural lining and epoxy resin lining. The asset granularity that is considered can also affect the number of alternatives available for that decision variable. Representing the network as small lengths of pipes increases the likelihood that areas of redundancy can be identified, thus representing cost savings. In this case, the size of the replaced main becomes the alternative.

12.2.3.1   Timing of the Action

The period of analysis being considered within the Methodology is 50 years. As with the identification of the alternatives, the temporal nature of the decisions can appear as an alternative of, or as, a decision variable. In the case of operational interventions, it is likely that decisions of a temporal nature will require additional decision variables with the alternatives representing the level of resources applied to that activity. Pipe assets, because of their long term nature require a single temporal decision on the timing of the intervention. This assumes only one action is undertaken over the period of analysis. It is suggested that this decision is considered separate to that which represents the intervention option. The alternatives for this additional decision variable are the time steps within the period of analysis.

This latter point introduces the concept of an intervention horizon within the period of analysis. The period of analysis defines the period where costs contribute to the calculation of the WLC. This can be considered to be independent of the time period where decisions need to be identified. Decision can be in respect of a sub-set of this period of analysis. An example of this is to formulate the problem such that only those actions required for the next 20 years are incorporated as decision variables. By still considering the cost stream over the period of analysis ensures that the decisions made over the 20-year period reflect the future operational savings. A further and simpler example is to consider what actions are required in the next five years (or the first time step). Therefore, decisions on the system today reflect the long term benefits.

12.3   Automated Search Technique

The search technique utilised in ExSoft is the genetic algorithm (GA). GAs (Holland, 1975; Goldberg, 1989) are new evolutionary computational techniques used to efficiently find optimal solutions in complex spaces (or problems). They utilise a non-random, non-deterministic search, meaning the solution space is not exploited in an entirely random manner. The GA commences by generating a random set (population) of possible solutions. Each solution then is assigned a value based on its appropriateness to a defined objective, for example, the objective functions provided in Equations 12.1 through 12.3. Another set of solutions are thus generated by using stochastic processes derived from those observed in nature. This continues until there is no further improvement in the set of solutions.

Before providing the mechanics behind the GA, it is worthwhile briefly explaining how a GA represents the decisions.

12.3.1 Representing the Problem

A GA utilises a string of decision variables as a means of representing the decision variables within a problem. An analogy, which explains the continual reference to nature, is that of a chromosome. The alternatives available for each decision are defined within each bit by its range of values. An example is that, for each set of pipe elements, two decisions need to be made, what to do and when to do it. These two decisions are represented by two integer values, the bounds of which are set by the number of available alternatives (i.e. a period of analysis of 50 years has 10 time periods, therefore the decision of when to do an activity is represented from 0 to 10). Thus, by collecting together these bits into a chromosome one represents an alternative operating and maintenance strategy.

12.3.2 How does a Genetic Algorithm Work?

Figure 12.1 provides a simplified representation of the steps in the application of GAs to any problem. As stated, a GA begins with the random generation of a set of chromosomes representing the initial population of solutions. The information in each chromosome is decoded and the worth of the solution measured. In the case here, the WLC of the water area is calculated for the identified alternatives for each decision variable, as defined in the chromosome. This worth, or WLC is assigned to the chromosome. Once this has been achieved for the full set, the iterative step of the GA begins.

Unlike other optimisation techniques a GA utilises a set of possible solutions. It attempts to evolve this set (or population) such that better solutions are generated. This evolution is achieved via two primary mechanisms, a selection and chromosome manipulation process. The selection process works on the basic assumption that if the chromosome of a worthy solution is manipulated, there exists a higher chance that a better solution results. Therefore, the selection technique chooses two chromosomes with a bias toward those more worthy, or with a lower WLC. This in essence is the non-random nature of the GA, instead of starting from scratch in generating the new population, it utilises the information already generated, in a stochastic and non-deterministic way.

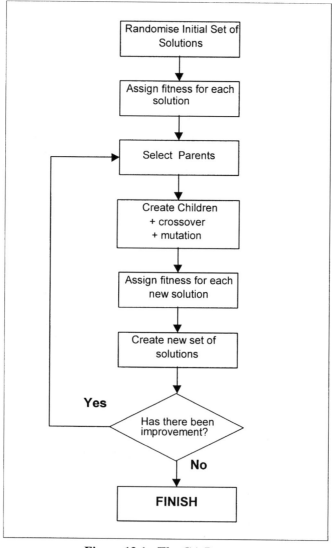

Figure 12.1: The GA Process

Two mechanisms are utilised to form new solutions (or children) from the selected parents. The first is crossover. This implies building two new child chromosomes by combining elements of the two parent chromosomes. The combination of the elements of the chromosome is stochastic, so there is no guarantee that improvement occurs. The other manipulative process is mutation. This process is essentially a random perturbation of one of the decision variables within the chromosome. Once generated, the worthiness (or the WLC) of the chromosome is calculated. A decision is then made on whether these two new chromosomes should be included in the set of new solutions. The process continues until no improvement is witnessed in the subsequent population. The use of the term "improvement" in the previous sentence is used loosely, rather a convergence criteria needs to be defined. As stated, there is no guarantee that at each step an improvement is obtained, therefore a convergence criteria may be the continual observance of no improvement.

This is a simple explanation of the mechanics of the optimisation technique. In each of the steps introduced the GA literature provides a myriad of different alternatives. There are a number of GA libraries available on the internet, ExSoft utilises the GA library held within the Centre for Water Systems at Exeter University, which provides various alternatives for each step of the process.

12.4   Decision Variables in the Case Study

To demonstrate the application of an automated search technique to a decision making process, the GA was applied to the case study system introduced in Chapter 11. For the example, the "Minimise the Whole Life Cost" objective of Equation 12.1 was assumed. The decision variables for this objective are the activities that can be undertaken to ensure the network meets the required serviceability (or performance) levels. In the Methodology there is clear distinction between activities based on whether they are operational or pipe interventions. In line with this, consideration is given over to each of these.

12.4.1 Operational Interventions

Operational interventions refer to activities that are undertaken across the whole network. In the example provided here, the decisions are made at the WSZ level, instead of the DMA level. This assumption is based on it being likely that if an activity is undertaken in one of the DMAs, it would also occur in the others. The alternatives for these operational interventions are whether resources are scheduled or not. How these activities are to be applied temporally were determined by providing three alternatives, namely;

1. the intervention activity occurs regardless of all other decisions (i.e. it is not a decision variable),
2. the operational activity occurs over the whole period of analysis, or does not,
3. a decision is required for each time period on whether the activity is to occur or not.

Of the four leakage interventions identified in Section 11.3, two were considered to fit into category 2. Pressure Reduction was assumed to fit into category 1. This is due to the fact that in England and Wales most DMAs have already been pressure managed, if there existed the scope to do so. "Additional Inspection" is assumed to imply that extra resources would have to be brought in to further drive down the leakage level. It was deemed unlikely that such an action would be required within each time step, therefore, the activity "Additional Inspection" is assumed to fall under the third category.

Given these assumptions, the chromosomal representation used within the GA is one bit representing whether resources should or should not be assigned to "Normal Leakage Detection" and "Detection and repair services to customers" for the period of analysis. Another way to portray this is, should these become normal company operational policies? The "Additional Inspection" is represented in the chromosome by a bit for each time period, representing whether the resources should be allocated for that activity. "Pressure Reduction" was assumed to be on regardless of the operating and maintenance regime, therefore it does not need to be represented as a decision variable.

12.4.2 Pipe Interventions

For the purposes of this demonstration it is assumed that the pipes within an operational area are aggregated together if they share the same material and diameter. Unlike the operational interventions, decisions are made for each class of pipes within each DMA. This increases the granularity and enables the pipes within the worst performing DMA to be targeted for intervention. Only replacement is considered in this example. The replacement of the mains can occur at any time throughout the period of analysis.

Due to the asset granularity, the replacement of the pipes was achieved through a like-for-like sizing. The replacement diameter size was chosen as that which is of "the nearest" size from the set provided below in Table 12.2. With the kind of granularity being observed in this analysis it is doubtful that downsizing mains would provide adequate service pressure in the area. Therefore, downsizing was not considered. Similarly, neither was the upsizing of mains.

Table 12.2: Set of Replacement Diameters

Diameter (mm)	C Value	Variable Private (£/m)
63.00	100	13.30
90.00	100	19.00
125.00	100	20.00
150.00	100	23.15
175.00	110	23.15
200.00	120	28.00
315.00	130	33.00
410.00	140	40.00

Table 12.2 provides the diameter, the updated "C"[2] value and the variable private cost of laying a metre of MDPE pipe. It was also assumed that there existed a fixed cost of replacement, to represent economies of scale. This large cost was implied if a pipe intervention action was to occur within that time period, the marginal cost of any subsequent activity within the area is equal to the value provided in the "Variable Private" column of Table 12.2.

There exist 12 pipe groups in one DMA, 15 in the other, each of which is represented by a single decision variable that denotes the timing of the intervention.

---

[2] The C value is the Hazen Willians roughness coefficient utilised in the hydraulic modelling of the water distribution network.

12.5   Automating the Decision Making for the Case Study System

Within ExSoft, the objective, the identification of the various decision variables, must be set in line with the discussions of Section 12.3. This was achieved through the "Decision Specification Form" element of Figure 10.2. The GA application resulted in the cost streams as provided in Figure 12.2.

Figure 12.2 provides five cost streams, including the private, social, total and its discounted cost streams. The fifth stream is for the capital expenditure that has been scheduled over the period of analysis. On comparison with the first cost stream presented in Chapter 11, which represents a no-intervention strategy, Figure 12.2 indicates that there is a substantial flattening of the total cost stream. The elements within the cost stream that shape the curves of Figure 12.2 are better understood by inspecting the cost streams provided in Figure 12.3. This figure provides the total private, the operating and the capital costs.

The difference between the private stream and the operating stream is equal to the regulatory penalties. In other words, even the so-called optimal maintenance strategy does not totally eliminate regulatory penalties. Further inspection indicates that these penalties are associated with the DG2 measure, or the properties at risk of receiving supply with insufficient pressure. There are two reasons why this penalty is still incurred. One is the assumption of 1% annual growth in demand. This may or may not be a reasonable assumption. A quick sensitivity of the network to this parameter indicates that if this growth in demand is halved, the DG2 penalty is eliminated.

The other point to keep in mind with this DG2 penalty is the fact that the mains are being replaced like-for-like often implying that the replacement diameter is slightly reduced. Although many existing mains (CI mains) would have small C values, much lower than the new mains, the downsizing of the mains means that there is not enough improvement to eliminate the DG2 penalty. However, there is a reduction in the number of properties at risk when compared to the no-intervention scenario.

Figure 12.4 provides the cost streams for the three main activities. It is interesting to see the breakdown of the costs across these three activities. The majority of the cost has been allocated to "Normal Supply", which is not surprising as this represents the majority of the at-boundary on-costs. The allocation across the leakage and burst activities remains relatively constant throughout the period of analysis.

The capital works undertaken in the system have come in two distinct steps. Initially a substantial amount of work is undertaken, which is followed up in the fourth time step by another tranche of works. This grouping together of the works is primarily a function of the large fixed cost that was assigned to any capital works undertaken in the system (as discussed in Section 12.3.1). This large fixed cost may or may not be representative of what occurs within a company, often out-sourcing contracts only contain a variable cost. Which is most appropriate will need to be determined for each case study.

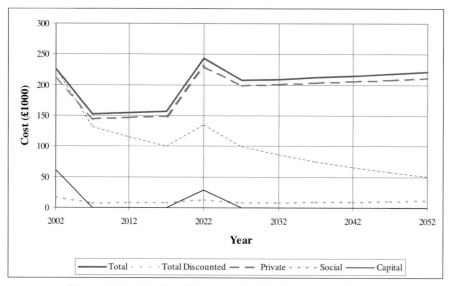

Figure 12.2: The Cost Stream after the GA Automation

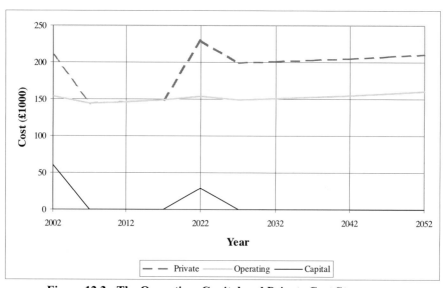

Figure 12.3: The Operating, Capital and Private Cost Streams

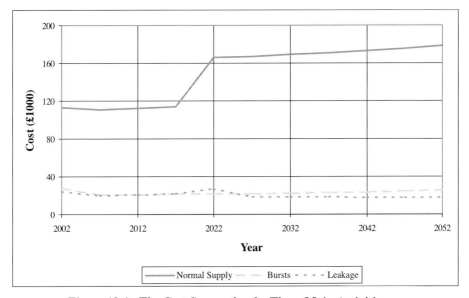

Figure 12.4: The Cost Stream for the Three Main Activities

12.6 Summary

This chapter has addressed the last level of the decision making process, its automation. It provides a valuable tool for modelling in greater detail the activities that should be undertaken over the period of analysis. Thus identifying possible sources for further efficiency gains that might otherwise be lost in the large amount of information that needs assimilating. However, for this to occur these efficiencies have to be reflected accurately in the input data.

It is for this reason that a caveat is added to applying this level of decision support. It should only be taken as the penultimate step, a full understanding should be attained in the information that is being input. The feedback loops identified and constructed into the overall decision making tool mean that the automated routines can play a role in this themselves.

A decision as complex as a WLC as discussed within this book will not be taken based on a single automated run. Rather it will be built up during each step of the Methodology, requiring each step to be revisited as more knowledge is gained by the decision-maker through each subsequent step. The "Decision Tool" within Methodology represents a tool, it will always require a decision-maker. However, as discussed it provides great value to the overall process, allowing a full investigation to identify efficiency gains.

Glossary

Abstraction	Procurement of water from either groundwater or surface water sources.
Activity Based Costing (ABC)	A process of individually listing and measuring the cost of each activity contributing to the production and delivery of a particular product or service.
Affected Customers	Customers affected by an incident.
Base Service Provision	The expenditure required to maintain the current level of serviceability to customers.
Burst	The structural failure of a main that requires or infers a repair action from the supervising water company.
Burst Complaints	The number of complaints that are received by an operator that can be linked to a burst pipe incident.
Burst Number	Number of burst pipes that require immediate or planned response by the water company.
Capex	Capital Expenditure.
Capital Expenditure	Money spent to acquire or upgrade physical assets.
Communication Pipe	Section of the service pipe that runs from the main to the point of delivery, usually the roadside stop tap.
Complaints	Negative enquiries relating to the quality or quantity of supply. Excludes billing or general enquiries.
Consumer	Number of service pipes.
Consumer Meters	Meters that register the quantity of water supplied to each customer.
Cost Driver	An attribute or performance measure of a water area that has been linked to the variable element of a cost.
Customers	Customers (household or business) billed by the company.
Customer Interruptions	An interruption to a customer's service.
Customer Interruption Hours	Number of hours for which customers experience an interruption to supply.
Discount Rate	The interest deducted in advance in purchasing, selling or lending a commercial paper.
Disinfection	The process of treatment undertaken to destroy microorganisms that can be detrimental to human health.
District Meter Area (DMA)	An area of a distribution network typically containing 2000 to 5000 properties (NWC/DoE, 1980) which is specifically defined, e.g. by the closure of valves, and in which the quantities of water entering and leaving the area are metered.

Enquiry	Any contact made by a customer to the company.
Environmental	Being concerned with the biophysical environment.
Externalities	Costs arising from the actions of the operator that are carried by either the environment or society.
Fixed Cost	A cost that does not vary with production levels.
Flushing Frequency	Number of times per year that a flushing operation is undertaken in the water area.
Inspections	Number of inspections of meters/fittings/installations/works required to follow up on complaints or work carried out.
Intervention	Any action that can be undertaken that will have an effect on the performance of the network or on an attribute that is identified as a driver for one of the input costs.
Leakage	The water which, having been obtained from a source, treated and put into supply, leaks or escapes other than by a deliberate or controllable action.
Leakage Target	The company specific leakage volume target set by the Regulator.
Life Cycle Accounting	Accounting for all the costs arising from the actions and consequences associated with the life cycle of a product.
Life Cycle Assessment	Studies the environmental aspects and potential impacts throughout the product's life (i.e. cradle to grave) from raw materials acquisition through production, use and disposal. The general categories of environmental impacts needing consideration include resource use, human health and ecological consequences (ISO14040).
Meters	Meters in the water area which measure flow volume (includes both consumer/customer and water company meters).
Operational Expenditure	Expenditure incurred in the operating of the infrastructure assets.
Opex	Operational expenditure.
Performance	Measure of the ability of the water network to fulfil its requirements.
Population	Population served by the water area.
Private Costs	Costs directly carried by the operator arising from their actions. Private costs include direct, indirect, hidden, contingent and image costs.
Private Sector	The part of a nation's economy which is not controlled by the government.
Projection	Quantitative estimate of future physical, economic or financial performance.

Public Costs	Costs resulting from an operator's action that are carried by society.
Public Sector	The part of the economy concerned which is controlled by the government.
Risk	Probability of an event occurring multiplied by its consequence.
Serviceability	A measure of the ability of the company to provide the service required by customers.
Service Density	The number of services per kilometre of main.
Service Pipes	Any pipe supplying water from a main to any premises and is subjected to water pressure.
Social	Relating to human society and its modes of organisation.
Societal Costs	Costs that accrue to society as a result of an activity.
Supply Pipe	Section of the service pipe that runs from the boundary stop tap to the first of practicable use by the customer.
Useful Life	The length of time that a depreciable asset is expected to be usable.
Variable Cost	A cost which depends on total volume or the extent of activity.
Water Area	Used to denote any discrete section of a water distribution network. It can be used to refer to either district meter area or a water supply zone.
Water Distribution Network	A network of underground pipes downstream of the service reservoir.
Water Supply Zone (WSZ)	A geographical aggregation of several DMAs.
Whole Life Costing (WLC)	Accounting system which considers all the costs (private and social) that accrue to its initiation, provision, operation, maintenance, servicing and decommissioning, over the useful life of an asset or a service.

Abbreviations

ABC	activity based costing
AC	asbestos cement
ACS	American Chemical Society
AMP	Asset Management Plan
API	associated programmers interface
AWWARF	American Water Works Association Research Foundation
AZNP	average zonal night pressure
BRE	Building Research Establishment
Capex	capital expenditure
CCWI	Computing and Control for the Water Industry (International Conf)
CI	cast iron
CVM	Contingent Value Method
DEFRA	Department for Environment, Food and Rural Affairs
DETR	Department of the Environment, Transport and the Regions
DG	Director General (of Ofwat)
DI	ductile iron
DMA	district meter area
DoE	Department of the Environment
DVGW	Deutche Vereinigung des Gas-und Wasserfaches
DWI	Drinking Water Inspectorate
EA	Environment Agency
EMAS	Environmental Management Audit System
EPA	Environmental Protection Agency (US)
FWR	Foundation for Water Research
GA	genetic algorithm
GIS	geographical information system
HEFCE	Higher Education Funding Council of England
ISO	International Standards Organisation
JPPSG	Joint Policy Procurement Strategy Group
LCA	life cycle assessment
LCC	life cycle costing
LCCM	life cycle cost management
LCCP	life cycle cost planning
LI	leakage index
LRMC	long run marginal cost
MDPE	medium density polyethylene
MIT	Massachusetts Institute of Technology
NAO	National Audit Office
NDPB	non-departmental public body
NFM	minimum night flow
NLCI	National Leakage Control Initiative
NOAA	National Ocenographic and Atmospheric Administration
NRR	natural rate of rise of leakage
NTU	nephelometric turbidity units
NWC	National Water Council
O&M	operation and maintenance

Ofwat	Office of Water Services
OGC	Office of Government Commerce
Opex	operating expenditure
PAH	poly-aromatic hydrocarbon
PCC	per capita consumption
PFI	private finance initiative
PPP	pollutor pays principle
PPP	public private partnership
PRV	pressure reducing valve
PVC	polyvinyl chloride
RAG	regulatory accounting guidelines
THM	tri-halomethane
TRL	Transport Research Laboratory
UFW	unaccounted for water
UKWIR	UK Water Industry Research
USEPA	United States Environmental Protection Agency
WAFU	water available for use
WHO	World Health Organisation
WLC	whole life cost(ing)
WLCF	Whole Life Costing Forum
WRc	Water Research Centre
WSZ	water supply zone

References

ACS (1998). "Understanding risk analysis: a short guide for health, safety, and environmental policy making: internet edition." A joint report by *American Chemical Society* and *Resources for the Future*, 39 pp., http://www.rff.org/misc_docs/risk_book.pdf.

Aihara, S. and Tateishi, A. (1994). "Upgrading of water distribution in Sapporo." *Water Supply Congress,* International Water Supply Association, 12 (Budapest (1/2)), 6-7, 6-11.

Anderson, M. J., Scott, R. and McManamon, P. (1997). "Applying condition and criticality to develop efficient inspection, maintenance and renewal programs." 17th AWWA Federal Convention, Melbourne, Australia, 674-679.

Andreou, S. A. and Marks, D. H. (1986). "Maintenance planning strategies for large diameter cast-iron mains." *AWWA Conference Synopsis*, 365-372.

Andreou, S. A., Marks, D. H. and Clark, R. M. (1987). "A new methodology for modelling break failure patterns in deteriorating water distribution systems: Theory." *Advanced Water Resources*, 10 (March), 2-10.

Anon. (1997a). "Optimizing investment in pipeline systems." Construction & Operation of Underground Utilities, February, 1-14.

Anon. (1997b). "Utilnets: System Guide and User Manual." Brite/Euram 11, Project No. 7210, May, 46 pp.

Arditi, D. and Messiha, H. M. (1999). "Life cycle cost analysis in municipal organisations". *Journal of Infrastructure Systems*, Vol 5(1), 1-10.

Arrow, K., Solow, R., Leamer, E., Radner, R. and Schuman, H. (1993). "Report of the NOAA panel on contingent valuation." *Federal Register*, 58(10), 4402-4614.

Arscott, A. and Grimshaw, F. (1996). "Evaluating investment in the water network on leakage detection." *IIR conference on "Cost Effective Management of Water Pipelines and Networks"*, London.

AWWARF (1996) "Internal Corrosion of Water Distribution Systems." AWWARF-DVGW.

Bayliffe, M. "What is Whole Life Asset Costing?" http://www.instem.com/news_events/whitepapers/wlac_mbayliffe.htm

Beck, U. (1992). *"Risk Society. Towards a New Modernity."* Sage, London.

Beim, G. K. and Hobbs, B. F. (1988). "Analytical simulation of water system capacity reliability - 2. A Markov chain approach and verification of the models." *Water Resources Research*, 24 (9), 1445-1458.

Bishop, R. C., Champ, P. A. and Mullarkey, D. J. (1995). *Contingent valuation in the handbook of environmental economics.* (Ed) Bromley, D. W. Blackwell, UK.

Boxall, J. B., Skipworth, P. J, and Saul, A. J. (2001). A novel approach to describing sediment movement in distribution mains, based on measured particle characteristics. *Accepted for CCWI Conference, 2001.*

Boxall, J. B., Skipworth, P. J., and Saul, A. J., (2002). Evaluation of mains flushing as a practical method for controlling discolouration events in distribution systems based on detailed field measurements. *Enviro 2002, Melbourne, Australia.*

Braden, J. and Kolstad, C. (eds) (1991). *Measuring the demand for environmental quality*. Amsterdam, North-Holland.

Brinker, B. J. (ed) (1994). *"Activity-based management, emerging practices in cost management."* Warren, Gorham & Lamont, Boston, MA.

Bromley, D. W. (ed) (1995). *Handbook of environmental economics*. Blackwell, Oxford, UK.

BS/ISO 15686 Buildings and constructed assets – service life planning. British Standards Institution.

Building Research Establishment (2000). Centre for whole life performance. http://bre.co.uk/whole_life

Bullinger, H-J., Warschat, J., Bopp, R. and Wörner, K. (1996). "Approaches to product life-cycle cost estimation in concurrent engineering." Institut Arbeitswirtschaft und Organisation (IAO), Stuttgart, Germany.

Butler, M. and West, J. (1987). "Leakage prevention and system renewal." *Pipeline Management Seminar, 1987, Pipeline Industries Guild.*

Chenery, C. (1984) Whole life cost of construction Informal Discussion – Structural Engineering Group. *Proc. Instn. Civ. Engrs.* Part 1, 76, 822-825.

Ciottoni, A. S. (1983). "Computerised data management in determining causes of water main failure." *12th International Symposium on Urban Hydrology, Hydraulics and Sediment Control*, University of Kentucky, Lexington, Kentucky, 323-329.

Clark, R. M., Stafford, C. L. and Goodrich, J. A. (1982). "Water distribution systems: a spatial cost evaluation." *Journal of Water Resources Planning and Management Division ASCE*, 108 (WR3), 243-255.

Conroy, P. J. (1997). "Achieving a cost effective rehabilitation solution." Chartered Institute of Water and Environmental Management Seminar on *The true cost of pipelines*, Swindon, UK, November, 1-7.

Conroy, P. J. and Hall, M. J. (1995). "Rehabilitation and leakage – a joint approach." *J. Water SRT - Aqua*, 44 (4), 196-201.

Constantine, G. and Darroch, J. (1995). "Predicting underground pipeline failure." *Water*, 2 (2), 9-10.

Cooper, R. (1990). Explicating the logic of ABC. *Management Accounting*, Nov, 58-60.

de Schaetzen, W., Randall-Smith, M. J., Savic, D. and Walters, G. A. (1998). "A genetic algorithm approach for rehabilitation in water supply systems." *International Conference on Rehabilitation Technology for the Water Industry*, Lille, France, 23-25 March, 1-11.

Deb, A. K., Hasit, Y. J., Grablutz, F. M. and Herz, R. K. (1998). "Quantifying future rehabilitation and replacement needs of water mains." AWWA Research Foundation, 156 pp.

DETR (1998). CIRM Business Plans: Construction Process. HMSO, http://www.construction.detr.gov.uk/cirm/busplan/proc

DETR (2000). Environmental valuation source list for the UK. http://www.environment.detr.gov.uk/evlist/01.htm

DETR (2000a). Departmental Procurement and Environmental Agenda, Circular 02/2000. DETR. http://www.environment.detr.gov.uk/greening/greenpro/circulars

DETR (2000b). "Resource Management Guidance – Procurement." DETR.

DETR (2001). "Review of work on whole-life environmental impacts of vehicles." HMSO http://www.roads.detr.gov.uk/cvtf/wholelife/

DETR/DWI (2000). "Annual compliance with drinking water quality parameters – an improved statistical approach", WRc Report to DETR/DWI, London, UK.

DWI (1998). "The 1999 Periodic Review of Prices and AMP3 : Further Guidance." *Drinking Water Inspectorate: Information Letter 13/98,* http://www.dwi.gov.uk/regs/infolett/1998/info1398.htm.

DWI (1999). "Drinking Water Quality – Comparative Measures." *Drinking Water Inspectorate: Information Letter 9/99,* http://www.dwi.gov.uk/regs/infolett/1999/info0999.htm.

DWI (2000a). "Determination of Requirements to meet new Lead Standards." *Drinking Water Inspectorate: Information Letter 12/2000,* http://www.dwi.gov.uk/regs/infolett/2000/info1200.htm.

DWI (2000b). "Drinking Water 1999." A Report by the Chief Inspector, Drinking Water Inspectorate, http://www.dwi.gov.uk/pubs/annrep99/index.htm.

DWI (2001). "Further Guidance on requirements to meet new lead standards." *Drinking Water Inspectorate: Information Letter 3/2001,* http://www.dwi.gov.uk/regs/infolett/2001/info0301.htm.

Dyachkov, A. (1994). "Rehabilitation of the water distribution in the city of Moscow." *Water Supply Congress,* International Water Supply Association, 12 (1/2, Zurich), 89-94.

E.A. (2000). *Water resource planning guidelines.* Environment Agency, Bristol, UK.

Edwards, D. (1998). *The Link Between Company Environmental and Financial Performance.* Earthscan Publications, London, UK.

Edwards, E., Sharp, B., Bancroft, G. and Dean, A. (1996). *Pipe failure predictor.* Internal report, School of Computing, Staffordshire University.

Emblemsvag, J. (2001). Activity-based life cycle costing. *Managerial Auditing Journal,* Vol 16(1).

Engelhardt, M. O. (1999). *"Development of a Strategy for The Optimum Replacement of Water Mains."* PhD, Department of Civil and Environmental Engineering, University of Adelaide, 514 pp.

Engelhardt, M. O., Skipworth, P. J., Savic, D. A., Saul, A. J. and Walters, G. A. (2000). "Rehabilitation strategies for water distribution networks: a literature review with a UK perspective." *Urban Water*, 2, 153-170.

Environment Act (1995)

European Commission (1998). Drinking Water Directive 98/83/EC. *Official Journal, L 330*, Brussels.

European Commission (2000) Water Framework Directive 2000/60/EC. *Official Journal, L 327, 2000.*

Evans, S. and McAloone, T. C. http://www.co-design.co.uk/economic.htm

Foundation for Water Research (1996). *Manual: Assessing the benefits of surface water quality improvements.* FR/CL 0005. Marlow, UK.

Francis, C. (1994). "Sieving the evidence on leakage." *Water and Waste Treatment,* DR Publications, London.

Freeman, A. Myrick (1993). *The measurement of environmental resource values: theory and methods.* Resources for the Future, Washington DC.

Goldberg, D. E. (1989). *Genetic Algorithms in Search optimization and Machine learning.* Addison-Wesley, Reading, Massachusetts.

Goulter, I. C. and Coals, V. (1986). "Quantitative approaches to reliability assessment in pipe networks." *Journal of Transport Engineering Division ASCE,* 112 (3), 287-301.

Goulter, I. C. and Kazemi, A. (1988). "Spatial and temporal groupings of water main pipe breakage in Winnipeg." *Canadian Journal of Civil Engineering,* 15, 91-97.

Grau, P. (1991). "Problems of external corrosion in water distribution systems." *Water Supply Congress,* International Water Supply Association, *International Reports,* 9 (3/4) 5-1, 5-45.

Greek, D. (1997). "Technological fingers in the dyke." *Professional Engineering,* Nov. 1997.

Habibian, A. (1994). "Effects of temperature on water main breaks." *Journal of Transportation Engineering Division ASCE,* 120 (2), 312-321.

Halhal, D., Walters, G. A., Ouzar, D. and Savic, D. A. (1997). "Water network rehabilitation with a structured messy genetic algorithm." *Journal of Water Resources Planning and Management Division ASCE,* 123 (3), 137-146.

Hanley, N. Shogren, J. F. and White, B. (1997). *Environmental economics in theory and practice.* MacMillan Press, Basingstoke, UK.

Haywood, V. H. et al. (1995). *Global biodiversity assessment.* United Nations Environment Programme. Cambridge University Press, UK.

Heal, G. M. (1981). *Economics and resources* In R. Butlin (ed) Economics of the Environment and Natural Resource Policy. Westview Press, Boulder, Colorado.

Heiskanen, E. (2000). Managers' interpretations of LCA: Enlightenment and responsibility or confusion and denial? *Business Strategy and the Environment* Vol 9, 239-254.

Herbert, H. (1994). "Technical and economic criteria determining the rehabilitation and/or renewal of drinking water pipelines." *Water Supply,* 12 (3/4, Zurich), 105-118.

Herz, R. K. (1996). "Ageing processes and rehabilitation needs of drinking water distribution networks." *J. Water SRT - Aqua,* 45 (5), 221-231.

Higher Education Funding Council for England (1998). Whole Life Costing: A good practice guide for end users and all those involved in the procurement process. http://archive.uwcm.ac.uk/uwcm/pr/jppsg/handbook/toolkit/wlc

Holland, J. H. (1975). *Adaption in natural and artificial systems.* University of Michigan, Ann Arbor, MI.

Innes, J. and Mitchell, F. (1990). *Activity based costing: a review with case studies.* Chartered Institute of Management Accountants, UK.

Jamieson, D. (1992). Ethics, public policy and global warming. *Science, Technology and Human Values,* Vol 17(2), 139-153.

Jarvis, M. J. and Hedges, M. R. (1994). "Use of soil maps to predict the incidence of corrosion and the need for iron mains renewal." *Journal of the Institution of Water Environment Management,* 8 68-75.

Joint Procurement Policy and Strategy Group (1996). Procurement Strategy for Higher Education. HMSO.

Kane, M. J. (1994). "Database to prioritise main rehabilitation." Hydrotop '94, Marseille, France, 201-213.

Kansal, M. L., Kumar, A. and Sharma, P. B. (1995). "Reliability analysis of water distribution systems under uncertainty." *Reliability Engineering and Safety Systems*, 50, 51-59.

Kessler, A., Ormsbee, L. and Shamir, U. (1990). "A methodology for least cost design of invulnerable water distribution networks." *Civil Engineering Systems*, 7 (1), 20-28.

Kettler, A. J. and Goulter, I. C. (1985). "An analysis of pipe breakage in urban water distribution networks." *Canadian Journal of Civil Engineering*, 12, 286-293.

Kim, J. H. and Mays, L. W. (1994). "Optimal rehabilitation model for water distribution systems." *Journal of Water Resources Planning and Management Division ASCE*, 120 (5), 674-691.

Kleiner, Y. and Rajani, B. (2000). "Considering time-dependant factors in the statistical prediction of water main breaks." *AWWA Infrastructure Conf. Proc.,* March 12-15, Baltimore, Maryland, USA.

Kleiner, Y., Adams, B. J. and Rogers, J. S. (1998). "Selection and scheduling of rehabilitation alternatives for water distribution systems." *Water Resources Research*, 34 (8), 2053-2061.

Lackington, D. W. and Burrows, B. L. (1994). "Criteria to determine appropriate levels of investment for rehabilitation." *Water Supply*, 12 (3/4, Zurich), 21-32.

Lambert, A. O. (1998). "A realistic basis for objective international comparisons of real losses from public water supply systems." *The Institution of Civil Engineers Conf., Water Environment 98 - Maintaining the Flow*, London.

Lamont, P. A. (1981). "Common pipe flow formulas compared with the theory of roughness." *AWWA Journal*, 73, 274-280.

Lansey, K. E., Basnet, C., Mays, L. W. and Woodburn, J. (1992). "Optimal maintenance scheduling for water distribution systems." *Civil Engineering Systems*, 9, 211-226.

Lei, J. and Sægrov, S. (1998). "Statistical approach for describing failures and lifetimes of water mains." *Water Science and Technology*, 38 (6), 209-217.

Li, D. and Haimes, Y. Y. (1992a). "Optimal maintenance related decision making for deteriorating water distribution systems -- 1. semi-Markovian model for a water main." *Water Resources Research*, 28 (4), 1053-1061.

Li, D. and Haimes, Y. Y. (1992b). "Optimal maintenance related decision making for deteriorating water distribution systems -- 2. multilevel decomposition approach." *Water Resources Research*, 28 (4), 1053-1061.

Loomis, J. B., (2000). "Environmental Valuation Techniques in Water Resource Decision Making." *Journal of Water Resources Planning and Management*, Vol 126, No. 6, November/December, 2000. 339-344.

Louws, P. (1997). "Risk/consequence approach to capital program prioritisation at City West Water." 17th AWWA Federal Convention, Melbourne, Australia, 780-783.

Maccarrone, P. (1998). Activity-based management and the product development process. *European Journal of Innovation Management* Vol 1 (3).

Marshall, P. (1999). "Evaluation of Long Term Performance: The Behaviour of Buried Pipes." *UKWIR*, Research No. 99/WM/20/12, 12.

Mavin, K. (1996). *"Predicting Pipe Failure Performance of Individual Water Mains."* Urban Water Research Association of Australia, Research Report No. 114, 189.

McAloone, T. C. and Evans, S. (1996). "The Economic Life-Cycle." *Co-Design, Special Issue: Green Design.* Issue 05/06 Open University Press, 76-80.

Mitchell, R. C. and Carson, R. T. (1989). *Using surveys to value public goods.* Cambridge University Press, UK.

Mukhopadhyay T. K. (1994). "Rehabilitation of old water supply pipes". *20th Water Engineering Development Centre Conference,* Colombo, Sri Lanka.

National Audit Office (2000). "Leakage and water efficiency." HMSO.

National Water Council/Department of the Environment (1980) Standing Technical Committee Report 26: Leakage control policy and practice.

O'Day, K. (1982). "Organizing and analysing leak and break data for making main replacement decisions." *Journal of the American Water Works*, 81 (10), 45-52.

O'Day, K. (1989). "External corrosion in distribution systems." *AWWA Journal*, 81 (10), 45-52.

O'Guin, M. (1990). Focus the factory with activity-based costing. *Management Accounting*, Feb 36-41.

Office of Government Commerce (2000). "Construction Procurement Guidance No 7 Whole Life Costs." Her Majesty's Stationery Office, London, UK.

Ofwat (1992). "RAG 4.01: Guideline for the analysis of operating costs and assets." Office of Water Services, UK.

Ofwat (1999). "RAG 3.04: Guideline for the content of regulatory accounts." Office of Water Services, UK.

Ofwat (2000a). "MD 161: Maintaining serviceability to customers." Office of Water Services, UK. http://ofwat.gov.uk/lettersmd/md161.htm

Ofwat (2000b). "Leakage and the Efficient Use of Water." Office of Water Services, UK. http://www.ofwat.gov.uk/pdffiles/ofleak.pdf

Ofwat (2001). RD 08/01 Review of drinking water quality aspects of serviceability relating to infrastructure and non-infrastructure assets.

Ofwat (2001a). "MD170: The role of the long-run marginal costs in provision and regulation of water services". Birmingham, UK.

Pascal, O. and Revol, D. (1994). "Renovation of water supply systems." *Water Supply Congress,* International Water Supply Association, 12 ((1/2) Budapest), 6-3, 6-7.

Pearce, D. W. and Moran, D. (1994). *The economic value of biodiversity.* Earthscan, London, UK.

Perman, R., Ma, Y. and McGilvray, J. (1996). Natural Resource & Environmental Economics. Longmans, UK.

PPK (1993). "Identification of Critical Water Supply Assets." UWRAA, Research Report No. 57, June, 131 pp.

Quimpo, R. G. and Shamsi, U. M. (1991). "Reliability based distribution system maintenance." *Journal of Water Resources Planning and Management Division ASCE*, 117 (3), 321-339.

Ramsey, F., (1928). "A mathematical theory of savings. £. *Economic Journal* 38.

Rouse, M. (2000). "New Drinking Water Regulations." Drinking Water Inspectorate, UK. http://www.dwi.detr.gov.uk/papers/newreg.htm.

Schaltegger, S. (1997). Economics of life cycle assessment: Inefficiency of the present approach. *Business Strategy and the Environment*, Vol 6, 1-8.

Schneiter, C. R., Haimes, Y. Y., Li, D. and Lambert, J. H. (1996). "Capacity reliability of water distribution networks and optimum rehabilitation decision making." *Water Resources Research*, 32 (7), 2271-2278.

Shamir, U. and Howard, C. D. D. (1979). "An analytic approach to scheduling pipe replacement." *AWWA Journal*, 71 (5), 248-258.

Sharp, W. W. and Walski, T. M. (1988). "Predicting internal roughness in water mains." *AWWA Journal*, 80 34-40.

Shore, D. G. (1988). "Economic optimization of distribution leakage control." *J. Institution of Water and Environmental Management,* Vol. 2 (No. 5), 545-551.

Skipworth, P. J., Saul, A. J. and Machell, J. (1999). "The effect of regional factors on leakage levels and the role of performance indicators to determine mandatory leakage targets." *Journal* of the Chartered Institute of Water and Environmental Management, Vol 13, June, 184-188.

Skipworth, P. J., Saul, A. J. and Engelhardt, M. O. (2000). Distribution network behaviour – extracting knowledge from data. *Int. Symp. on Water Network Modelling for Optimal Design and Management,* Woodbury Park, UK.

Smith, J .A. (1992). An examination of recent developments in leakage control monitoring techniques. *J. Water Supply*, Vol. 10, Florence.

Sohal, A. S. and Chung, W. W. C. (1998). Activity based costing in manufacturing: two case studies on implementation. *Integrated Manufacturing Systems*, Vol 9(3).

Tsui, E. and Judd, G. (1991). "Statistical Modelling of Water Main Failures." *UWRAA*, Research Report No.33, 33.

UK Water Industry (1994). "Managing Leakage" series of reports, published by WRc.

UKWIR (1997). "Effects of Climate Change on River Flows and Groundwater Recharge: Guidelines for Resource Assessment." *Report Ref. No. 97/CL/04/1.*

UKWIR (1998). "Quantification of Serviceability." *UKWIR*, Research Ref. No. 98/RG/01/1, 96.

UKWIR (1999). "The natural rate of rise of leakage." *Report Ref. No. 99/WM/08/22.*

UKWIR (2002). "A Common Framework for Capital Maintenance Planning." *Report Ref No. 02/RG/05/3*. On website www.ukwir.org.uk.

USEPA (1995). An Introduction to Environmental Accounting As A Business Management Tool: Key Concepts And Terms. *Office of Pollution Prevention and Toxics*, USEPA, Washington, D.C.

Vincent, D., Read, M. and McManamon, P. (1997). "Strategic water supply project evaluation utilising a practical assessment of risk." 17th AWWA Federal Convention, Melbourne, Australia, 16-21 March, 731-736.

Walski, T. M. (1982). "Economic analysis for rehabilitation of water mains." *Journal of Water Resources Planning and Management Division ASCE*, 108 (WR3), 296-307.

Walski, T. M. (1985). "Cleaning and lining versus parallel mains." *Journal of Water Resources Planning and Management Division ASCE*, 111 (1), 43-53.

Walski, T. M. (1987a). *"Water Supply System Rehabilitation."* New York, Task Committee on Water Supply System Rehabilitation, ASCE.

Walski, T. M. (1987b). "Discussion on: multi-objective optimisation of water distribution networks by I. C. Goulter." *Civil Engineering Systems*, 4 (4), 215- 217.

Walski, T. M. and Pelliccia, A. (1982). "Economic analysis of water main breaks." *AWWA Journal*, 74 (March), 140-147.

Walski, T. M., Wade, R., Sharp, W. W., Sjostrom, J. W. and Schlessinger, D. (1986). "Conducting a pipe break analysis for a large city." *AWWA Conference Symposium*, 387-402.

Water Act (Privatisation) (1989)

Water Industry Act (1991)

Water Resources Act (1991)

Water Supply (Water Quality) Regulations 1989, SI No. 1384 Water, England and Wales, http://www.dwi.gov.uk/regs/si1384/1384.htm.

Water Supply (Water Quality) Regulations 2000, SI No. 1297, Water Industry, England and Wales, http://www.dwi.gov.uk/regs/si1297/1297.htm.

Welford, R. (1995). *Environmental strategy and sustainable development: the corporate challenge*. Routledge. London. UK.

Wood (2000). A personal communication arising out of a conversation with Mr Wood, TRL.

Xu, C. and Goulter, I. C. (1998). "Probabilistic model for water distribution reliability." *Journal of Water Resources Planning and Management Division ASCE*, 124 (4), 218-228.